Other Titles of Interest

35 OPTO-DISPLAY TERMINAL BLOCK PROJECTS

by

ROY BEBBINGTON, MISTC

BERNARD BABANI (publishing) LTD
THE GRAMPIANS
SHEPHERDS BUSH ROAD
LONDON W6 7NF
ENGLAND

Please Note

Although every care has been taken with the production of this book to ensure that any projects, designs, modifications and/or programs, etc., contained herewith, operate in a correct and safe manner and also that any components specified are normally available in Great Britain, the Publishers do not accept responsibility in any way for the failure, including fault in design, of any project, design, modification or program to work correctly or to cause damage to any other equipment that it may be connected to or used in conjunction with, or in respect of any other damage or injury that may be so caused, nor do the Publishers accept responsibility in any way for the failure to obtain specified components.

Notice is also given that if equipment that is still under warranty is modified in any way or used or connected with home-built equipment then that warranty may be void.

British Library Cataloguing in Publication Data

A catalogue record for this book is available from the British Library

ISBN 0 85934 410 X

Cover designed by Gregor Arthur
Printed and bound in Great Britain by Cox & Wyman Ltd, Reading

Preface

All the projects described in this book either respond to light, or produce light for indication or display purposes. In line with the companion books: '45 Simple Electronic Terminal Block Projects', and '30 IC Terminal Block Projects', all projects can be built on screw-terminal blocks without the need for soldering. In addition, in the interests of beginners and younger students, power requirements do not extend beyond a perfectly harmless 9-volt battery.

The 35 projects have been graded in level of complexity to enable readers to work gradually through some simple circuits before tackling the more ambitious projects. Again, both theoretical circuit and layout diagrams have been included. Although the beginner will tend to work from the layout diagram, the experienced constructor will probably find the circuit diagram more informative. For a better understanding of electronic circuits, time will be well spent in studying and comparing both circuit and layout diagrams. Although the natural progression is from simple circuits using a few components, to transistor circuits and integrated circuits, in practice, because circuits are 'integrated' comparatively few extra components are needed.

Most projects have been approached from the 'fun' aspect although the commercial or industrial applications have not been completely ignored. A counter may be just a mundane counter, but give it something interesting to count or add a few Christmas decorations and it becomes much more imaginative. A storage register can hold more interesting things than cold calculating numbers!

The projects mainly use light-emitting diodes (LEDs), single, bi-colour, tri-colour, axial, and flashing types to produce visual indicators and 'light'-entertainment.

Light-dependent resistors (LDRs) are used for sensing, and seven-segment LED circuits are also included for simple number and letter displays. Pins of a 0.3in display (Maplin) will fit in a standard 14-pin DIL socket.

Roy Bebbington

Contents

Chapter 1

OPTO-DEVICES AND COMPONENTS

You may already be familiar with the opto-electrical devices and other components that are used in these projects, but if you are not, then it's worth getting to know what you are looking at, or looking for. The physical shapes of most of the components used will be revealed in the layout diagrams that accompany each project, but here is a run-down on the most commonly used components that you will encounter.

Light-Emitting Diodes

Figure 1 is a "rogues' gallery" of the various light-emitting diodes (LEDs) that are used in the projects described. LEDs are made of semiconductor material such as gallium arsenide that emits light when the anode is about 2 volts positive with respect to the cathode. This voltage should not be exceeded and a series resistance is often required to reduce the voltage applied and limit the current to preferably less than 20 mA.

Standard LEDs (Fig.1a)

These are available in several colours, shapes and sizes. The popular round types shown in Figure 1 are 5mm diameter, but different sizes (3mm and 10mm diameters) and flat stackable LEDs are also available in red, green, orange and yellow. The cathode (k) is usually identified by the flat chamfered edge adjacent to its shorter lead. On most LEDs, it is also possible to spot the larger electrode which is the cathode. If still unsure, connect the LED in series with a 680-ohm resistor to a 9V battery. Reverse the battery if the LED does not light. When lit, the lead nearest the battery positive (+) is the anode. Most standard LEDs operate on a nominal forward voltage of 2V, but some, advertised as 5V and 12V types, have built-in limiting resistors for direct connection across these higher voltage supplies.

An arrangement of four standard 2V LEDs in series with a suitable current-limiting resistor is shown in Figure 2; the method of calculating the limiting resistor is also given.

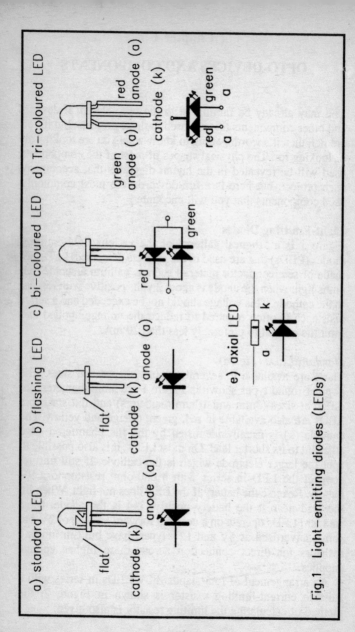

Fig.1 Light-emitting diodes (LEDs)

a) standard LED

flat

cathode (k)

anode (a)

b) flashing LED

flat

cathode (k)

anode (a)

c) bi-coloured LED

red   green

d) Tri-coloured LED

red anode (a)

cathode (k)

green anode (a)

green

a

red

a

e) axial LED

a   k

2

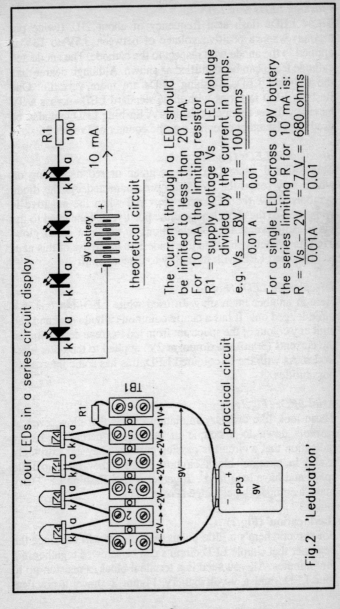

four LEDs in a series circuit display

R1
100

10 mA

9V battery

k a k a k a k a

theoretical circuit

The current through a LED should be limited to less than 20 mA.
For 10 mA the limiting resistor
R1 = supply voltage Vs – LED voltage divided by the current in amps.

e.g. $\dfrac{Vs - 8V}{0.01\ A} = \dfrac{1}{0.01} = 100\ ohms$

For a single LED across a 9V battery the series limiting R for 10 mA is:

$R = \dfrac{Vs - 2V}{0.01A} = \dfrac{7V}{0.01} = 680\ ohms$

practical circuit

R1

k a k a k a k a
LD1 LD2 LD3 LD4

TB1

1 2 3 4 5 6

2V→ ←2V→ ←2V→ ←2V→ ←1V→

9V

9V
PP3
– +

Fig.2 'Leducation'

3

Flashing LEDs (Fig.1b)

These LEDs flash at a frequency of about 2Hz (twice per second) when a positive voltage of between 3.5V to 13V is applied to the anode with respect to the cathode. The anode and cathode leads can be identified as shown. Although dearer than the standard LEDs, flashing LEDs are more versatile. One flashing LED in series with three standard LEDs across a 9V battery will set them all flashing. A flashing LED can also be used to pulse other circuits, e.g. the counter of Project 26.

Bi-coloured LEDs (Fig.1c)

This diffused white LED glows green or red depending on which way round the two leads are connected. As the diode symbols show, the LED will glow red when the negative is connected to the short lead and the positive is connected to the long lead; reverse these connections to obtain a green glow. You can probably think up a few ideas to make use of this neutral-coloured LED with its ability to detect polarity.

Tri-coloured LEDs (Fig.1d)

Here is another interesting diffused white LED, but this is a three-legged one. It has a centre common cathode lead and can emit any colour of the spectrum from red to green depending on the currents (30mA maximum at 2V) applied to the outer electrodes. As with the bi-coloured LED, this has some interesting possibilities.

Axial LEDs (Fig.1e)

These look like ordinary miniature diodes that glow, even at currents down to a couple of milliamps; perhaps a handy indication that a circuit is passing current. They are extremely useful in terminal block circuits because they take up little space and have long leads. Together with a flashing LED they make a compact lapel badge (Project 11).

'Leducation' (Fig.2)

For starters, here's a little bonus project that will convince the beginner that simple LED circuits can be screwed together in a few minutes. All you need is a terminal block, a resistor, up to four LEDs and a 9-volt battery. Figure 2 shows a practical wiring diagram and its equivalent theoretical circuit. It also explains how to limit the current through the LED and the voltage across it with an appropriate dropping resistor. Replace one of the standard LEDs with a flashing LED in this series arrangement and the other three will flash in sympathy. Notice that you can connect a flashing LED directly across the 9V battery without the need of a limiting resistor; this useful effect has been exploited in some of the later projects.

Resistors (Fig.3)
Resistors control the flow of current in a circuit depending on their value in ohms, kilohms (thousands of ohms) or megohms (millions of ohms).

Fixed resistors (Fig.3a)
The list shows how fixed resistors are colour-coded. The three bands at one end of a resistor denote its value in ohms. Reference to the code will confirm that if the bands read from the end are red, violet, orange, the value is 2 (red), 7 (violet), and 3 (orange) noughts, i.e. 27,000 ohms or 27 kohms. Similarly, the colour code for a million ohms, referred to as 1M, would be brown, black, green. The tolerance of a resistor is normally indicated by a fourth band, gold ±5%, silver ±10%.

Potential dividers (Fig.3b)
Variable resistors are used in some projects where for instance the timing needs to be changed or a voltage level has to be set. These potentiometers, or 'pots' as they are often called, consist of a carbon resistance track varied by a slider contact. A potentiometer has three contacts; a potential difference connected between the outer contacts can be varied and tapped off between the slider and one of the other contacts, as with a volume control. Some applications, where only a variable resistance is required, use only the centre wiper and one of the outer contacts.

Light-depending resistors (Fig.3c)
Light-depending resistors (LDRs), sometimes called photo-conductive cells (PCCs), are made from photo-sensitive materials, the resistance of which change in value when

a) Fixed Resistors

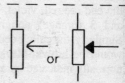

1 2 3

Resistors are used to control the flow of electrons (current) around a circuit.
The coloured bands denote the value in ohms.
1st band = first significant figure
2nd band = second significant figure
3rd band = number of noughts;i.e multiplier

Colour code:
- 0 black
- 1 brown
- 2 red
- 3 orange
- 4 yellow
- 5 green
- 6 blue
- 7 violet
- 8 grey
- 9 white

b) Potential Dividers

Uses all three tags of a variable resistance.
The voltage on the slider will vary between the voltages at the two ends.

c) Light-dependent resistors (LDRs)

Light falling on an LDR causes its resistance to fall. In darkness its resistance is several megohms, in bright sunlight it is about 200 ohms.

Fig.3 Resistors

6

a) Capacitors

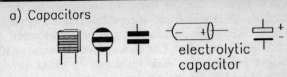

electrolytic
capacitor

Stores electrical charge. Larger values are
electrolytics. Connect the right way round.

b) Diodes

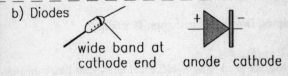

wide band at   anode   cathode
cathode end

Diodes conduct in one direction only,
so can be used to rectify a.c. waveforms.

c) Transistors

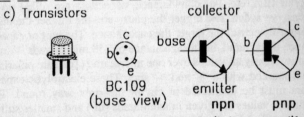

collector

base

c
b   c
b
e   e
BC109   emitter
(base view)   npn   pnp

A device which can be used to switch or amplify.
npn transistors work with the collector positive
with respect to the emitter (reverse for pnps).

d) Integrated Circuits

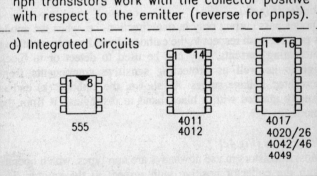

555

1   14
4011
4012

1   16
4017
4020/26
4042/46
4049

Fig.4   Capacitors, Diodes, Transistors, ICs

exposed to light. A zig-zag thread of cadmium sulphide is deposited on an insulator and encapsulated in a transparent resin. The ORP12 photoconductive cell has a resistance of about 2.5k at 50 lux, which falls to less than 200 ohms at 100 lux, bright sunlight. Its dark resistance is about several megohms. An LDR can be used as a light sensor to switch on/off a light, a relay, or to operate an alarm.

Capacitors, Diodes, Transistors, ICs (Fig.4)

Capacitors (Fig.4a)

Capacitors are used to store electrical energy, to block unwanted signals, to select and tune in wanted signals. Basically, they consist of two metal plates with an insulator sandwiched in between. This insulator can be air, paper, polystyrene, mica, mylar film, etc. For convenience, capacitors are rolled up to conserve space. The bigger the plates and the thinner the insulator (dielectric) the larger the capacitance. The unit of capacitance is the farad, but a capacitance of 250 microfarads is quite large. Nearly all values over one microfarad (1μF) are polarised and marked with a '+' and '−' sign. These electrolytic capacitors must be connected in circuit the right way round. The smaller values are given in nanofarads (nF) and smaller still in picofarads (pF).

Diodes (Fig.4b)

Diodes pass current only in one direction, i.e. when the anode is positive with respect to the cathode. In addition to rectifying alternating currents, they can be used to detect or to block signals as well as protecting sensitive components from unwanted voltage surges. As shown, the cathode (k) end is usually marked with a black band to distinguish it from the anode (a).

Transistors (Fig.4c)

Most transistors in use nowadays are npn types, which operate with the collector positive with respect to the emitter. The general-purpose BC109 listed is a low-noise high-gain amplifier that can also be used to switch signals or as an oscillator.

8

Integrated circuits (Fig.4d)

The integrated circuits (ICs) shown here are 8-way, 14-way and 16-way dual-in-line (d.i.l.) chips that each contain many transistor circuits. This means that although these circuits are much more complex, a lot of the construction work has already been done in these tiny building blocks. Suitable d.i.l. holders need to be made up with short connecting leads, so initially you may need to ask a favour of dad, mum or any friend or relative who wields a soldering iron. There may be other components with tags, for example, potentiometers, speakers, switches that need short flexible leads attaching; soldering is more permanent than wire-wrapping.

WARNING

CHILDREN MUST NEVER ATTEMPT SOLDERING BY THEMSELVES WITHOUT AN EXPERIENCED PERSON SUPERVISING.

Chapter 2

TERMINAL BLOCKS AND
WIRING TECHNIQUES

Moulded plastic terminal block strips are readily available from the electrical departments of most DIY stores. They are also listed in the Maplin catalogue as 12-way flexible moulded terminal block strips: 2A (order code FE78K) and 5A (order code HF01B). They normally cost under £1. These may be easily cut into shorter lengths if required. The narrower spacing of the 2A strip size is preferred for components with short leads.

A 12-way terminal block connector is also listed, which could be useful for quick connection/disconnection of circuit leads where necessary. It consists of one block with a screw terminal and plug per position, and another block with a screw terminal and mating socket per position. These may also be cut into shorter lengths.

Most of the simpler projects can be easily housed on one terminal block strip, and if a project is to be a permanent fixture, any surplus terminal pairs can be reclaimed and used for other projects or extension connectors. This salvage operation also applies to components. As these are not mutilated by the screw-in method, no soldering or cutting the connecting leads short, most components may be reclaimed in pristine condition for re-use. For clarity, some of the connecting wires on the layout diagrams are shown extra long. However, it is advisable to keep all leads as short as practical; let them cross over the terminal blocks if necessary. Use plastic sleeving on bare wires, or plastic-covered wire for the links to prevent short-circuits. Make sure that the ends on insulation-covered wire are trimmed back about 1cm so that the copper wire is firmly gripped by the terminal screw. A small, flat-bladed screwdriver should be selected that suitably matches the diameter of the terminal screw-heads. Additional two-terminal, single-way strips can be used if required to extend component leads. Figure 5 illustrates some of these tips for terminal blocks. Note that a switch can be made from two pieces of springy wire in adjacent screw terminals.

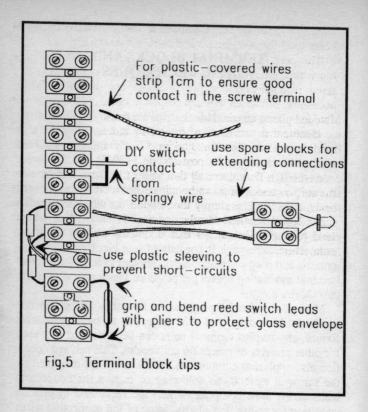

For plastic-covered wires strip 1cm to ensure good contact in the screw terminal

DIY switch contact from springy wire

use spare blocks for extending connections

use plastic sleeving to prevent short-circuits

grip and bend reed switch leads with pliers to protect glass envelope

Fig.5 Terminal block tips

The more advanced projects built around integrated circuits use either 8-pin, 14-pin or 16-pin integrated circuits so it is advisable to make up three separate breadboard layouts, one for each type of IC. For convenience, the terminal blocks TB1, TB2, and d.i.l. holders for the ICs should be mounted on a piece of plywood or chipboard measuring approximately 18 ×12 cm. This means that the layout diagrams for the projects are generally shown full size.

The blocks can be either screwed or tacked to the board; the short plastic-covered copper leads from the terminals to the IC-holder are sufficient to ensure that the IC is held rigidly. These layouts together with the pin numbering for the relevant ICs can be seen in the projects of Chapter 5. The inner terminals are mainly reserved for the IC pin connections, the outer terminals being used for components and supply connections.

The wire ends on resistors, capacitors, diodes, LEDs, transistors, etc., will in most cases be long enough to bridge the screw-in connections shown in the layout diagrams. Where necessary, additional terminal strips can be added to accommodate extra long connections.

If more than one IC is used in a circuit, a breadboard can be made up with two ICs wired between TB1 and TB2, or alternatively, two separate breadboard layouts can be linked.

Some IC s do not use all the connecting pins. If necessary, the surplus terminal(s) can be utilised for other circuit connections if required by simply unscrewing and disconnecting the redundant flying lead attached to the IC holder. This surplus lead can be coiled up so that it does not short-circuit any connections.

Chapter 3

SIMPLE OPTO-PROJECTS

These projects provide a gentle lead-in to illustrate the method of connecting various LEDs and basic components on to terminal blocks. Most projects can be screwed together in a matter of minutes. Success with these simple circuits will not only inspire confidence, but will no doubt encourage new-comers in electronics to attempt the more ambitious projects using transistors and integrated circuits.

Project 1 – Light Telegraph

That adventure story cliche, "A flashing signal lamp stabbed the darkness ... ", never fails to stir the imagination of young readers, and this first circuit offers the possibility to stir a few of those youthful imaginations. The Light Telegraph enables two operators to send messages to each other using a single LED that flashes either red or green depending on the sender. The LED flashes orange for 'combined operations' – warning that both operators are sending at the same time. Operators can agree on their own codes, but the traditional Morse Code is given in Figure 33.

Apart from signalling, another use for this circuit is in quiz games as a simple precedence switch. As the first contestant with an answer to a question presses a pushbutton, the LED is switched to glow either red or green. However, the quiz con-troller must check which colour quickly, as it will change to orange if the second contestant subsequently presses. Obviously, split second decisions are difficult to observe by this simple method, but an initial orange glow indicates a dead heat, i.e. both switches operated simultaneously.

The simple ingredients are two pushbutton switches, one tri-colour LED, a resistor, a battery, a 5-way terminal block and a metre or so of insulated connecting wire.

Circuit (Fig.6)

The two diodes of the tri-colour LED D1 are each in series with one of the pushbutton switches S1, S2. The common limiting resistor R1 drops the 9V battery supply to the requisite 2V for the LED. Switch S1 activates the red diode and S2 activates the green diode. As mentioned, if both S1 and S2 switches are operated simultaneously the LED glows orange.

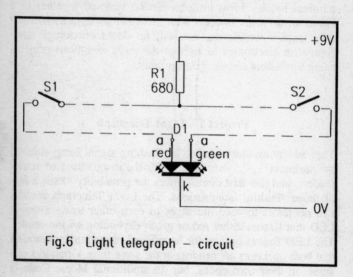

Fig.6 Light telegraph – circuit

Layout (Fig.7)

The diagram needs little comment except to say that all the plastic-covered connecting leads should be stripped back for about 1cm to ensure good electrical connection with the screws in the terminal block. Twin flex can be used between TB1 and the two switches, the length depending on the distance between the intended operating positions. Remember that D1 must be in line-of-sight of both operators. For rigidity, it may be better to mount TB1 on a small block of plywood.

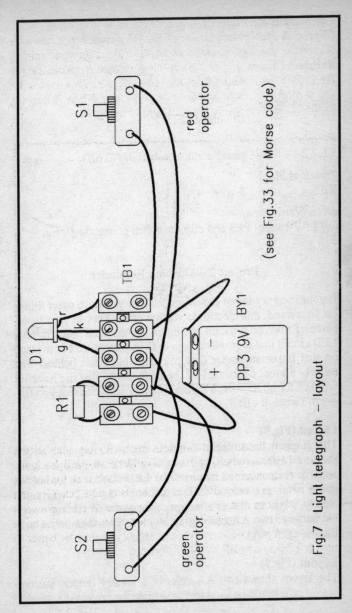

S1

red
operator

(see Fig.33 for Morse code)

TB1

r
k
g

D1

R1

PP3 9V

BY1

−

+

S2

green
operator

Fig.7 Light telegraph – layout

17

Components for Project 1
(Figs. 6 & 7)

Resistor
R1   680

Semiconductor
D1   tri-colour LED

Switches
S1, S2   pushbutton, non-locking (2 off)

Terminal Block
TB1   5-way

Miscellaneous
BY1 9V battery PP3 and clip, insulated connecting wire.

Project 2 – Flashing Reminder

If your memory is not too dependable or you have other things
on your mind, this electronic version of the knot in your hand-
kerchief may be a useful reminder. It's an economic flashing
LED circuit that is small enough to fit in your pocket or to stand
on that important paper that you must not leave behind. The
miserly current consumed by the LED means that the batteries
will last for hours – even if your memory is so bad that you for-
get to switch it off!

Circuit (Fig.8)
This is easily the simplest circuit in the book, requiring only a
flashing LED, a switch, and a battery. When these three components are connected in series the LED flashes on and off at
about twice per second (2Hz). Although the LED was suffi-
ciently bright to attract attention, the measured current with a
3V battery (two AA cells in series) was less than half a mil-
liamp (< 0.5 mA).

Layout (Fig.9)
The layout shows two AA cells in a battery holder, but two
button cells could be used to miniaturise the project if a suitable

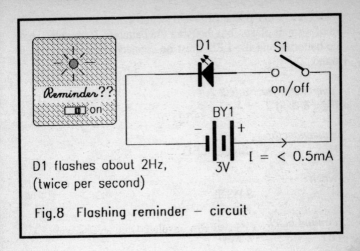

D1 flashes about 2Hz,
(twice per second)

Fig.8 Flashing reminder — circuit

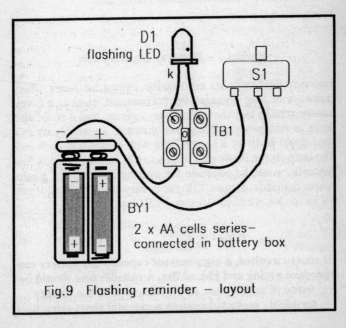

Fig.9 Flashing reminder — layout

19

holder is available. The LED and switch can be mounted on the lid of a small plastic box housing the batteries. Remember that the batteries and the LED must be connected the correct way round.

Components for Project 2
(Figs. 8 & 9)

Semiconductor
D1   flashing LED

Switch
S1   S.P.S.T.

Terminal block
TB1   2-way

Miscellaneous
BY1 3V battery with holder, small plastic case.

Project 3 – Two-way Light Switch

Two-way light switches are familiar around the house where stairways or long passages are encountered. Here is a 6-volt battery version that shows how they operate, and it could also serve as emergency lighting. For instance, a garden path to a shed could be lit by a central light with a switch at each end. The lamp shown draws only 40mA so a battery holder with four AA cells would be adequate for intermittent use. For greater power demands, a spare 12V car battery could be used if two 6V lamps are wired in series or a 12V lamp is used.

WARNING!
If short-circuited, a high-current capacity car battery can produce arcing and risk of fire. A suitable fuse should be wired in series, close to the battery, and the battery terminals protected against accidental short-circuit.

Circuit (Fig.10)

Two-way switching is achieved by connecting the outer contacts of S1, one of the two changeover switches, to the other, S2. With the switches in the position shown, the series path around the circuit is completed and LP1 is switched on. Operate either of the switches and the circuit will be broken. From this it will be obvious that the lamp can be switched on or off by either switch, independent of the position of the other.

Layout (Fig.11)

The layout will largely depend on the application, but generally it is useful to have a 3- or 4-way terminal block at each end to provide the switch connections and to take care of the lamp and battery connections. Extra terminal block connections can be used if the connecting leads need to be extended. If the wiring is external, make sure the wiring and connections are well insulated.

WARNING!
KEEP ALL THESE LOW-VOLTAGE CIRCUITS WELL
AWAY FROM ANY MAINS WIRING.

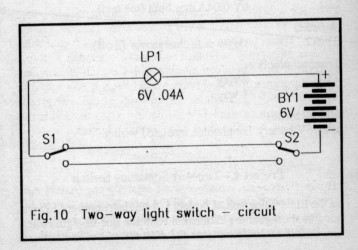

Fig.10 Two-way light switch – circuit

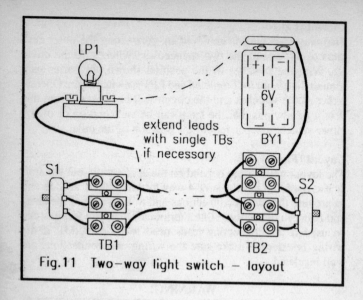
Fig.11 Two-way light switch – layout

Components for Project 3
(Figs. 10 & 11)

Lamp
LP1   6V 0.04A mes bulb (see text)

Switches
S1, S2   single-pole changeover (2 off)

Terminal blocks
TB1   3-way
TB2   4-way

Miscellaneous
BY1 6V battery, lampholder, insulated wiring.

Project 4 – Two-way Signalling Switch

In the Light Telegraph of Project 1, a single tri-colour LED was used as the signalling element; a common line-of-sight indicator, which naturally restricts the distance and vision between

22

operators. However, this project uses an LED at both ends of the link so that line-of-sight is not necessary. If your link is long enough then there is no reason why you cannot communicate to someone in another room or to your friend next door, providing that you have devised some means of attracting his or her attention in the first place.

Circuit (Fig.12)

The circuit is similar to the previous two-way switch except that two series LEDs are used with a limiting resistor. Two pushbutton changeover switches are used for S1 and S2, the interconnections being arranged so that the circuit is normally broken with the pushbuttons released. The values of the limiting resistor for a 6V or a 9V battery are shown. Both LEDs D1 and D2 are operated when either S1 or S2 is depressed.

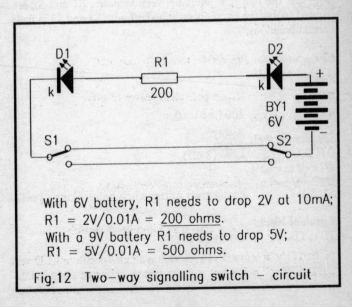

With 6V battery, R1 needs to drop 2V at 10mA;
R1 = 2V/0.01A = 200 ohms.
With a 9V battery R1 needs to drop 5V;
R1 = 5V/0.01A = 500 ohms.

Fig.12 Two–way signalling switch – circuit

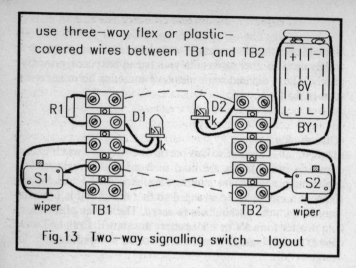

use three—way flex or plastic—
covered wires between TB1 and TB2

R1   D1   D2   6V   BY1

S1   S2

wiper   TB1   TB2   wiper

Fig.13 Two—way signalling switch — layout

Layout (Fig.13)

The arrangements of the two 5-way terminal blocks are shown.
Note that the two link wires between switches S1 and S2 are
crossed so that the circuit is switched off with S1 and S2 in their
normal positions.

Components for Project 4
(Figs. 12 & 13)

Resistor
R1   200 (see text)

Semiconductors
D1, D2   LED (2 off)

Switches
S1, S2   changeover microswitch non-locking (2 off)

Terminal blocks
TB1, TB2   5-way (2 off)

Miscellaneous
BY1 6V battery, insulated wiring

Project 5 – Initial and Number Selector

Digital letters and numbers formed by LED segments are widely used on clock radios, TV sets and video recorder display panels. These alphanumeric displays are often formed by 7-segment LEDs arranged in the shape of a number eight. In these devices the characters are presented automatically via decoding circuits. Here, as an introduction, we can see how each character can be produced by manually connecting the appropriate segments of the LED. This static method of presentation obviously limits the possibilities of these devices, but it does enable simple initials or numbers to be displayed; for instance, someone's initial, a '0' and a '1' or a 'h' (heads) and a 't' (tails) suggest some useful characters. These displays are commercially available in several sizes (0.3in to 4in) and colours; several can be used to increase the message length. If 7-segment displays capture your interest, then Project 25 offers a more versatile display driven by a decoder.

Circuit (Fig. 14)

The circuit shows a common anode 7-segment LED supplied by a 3V battery via a small dropping resistor. One or more of the segment cathodes, usually labelled 'a' to 'g', may be connected together and routed via R1 to the 0V rail. The example shows the connections for the capital letter 'A'. Adding the segment 'd' to the rest would naturally turn this into an '8'. As indicated, all the numbers from 0 to 9 are available as well as certain upper and lower case letters. Ideally, separate limiting resistors would be preferred to maintain uniform brightness, but this simple circuit serves to demonstrate the principle.

Layout (Fig. 15)

The suggested layout shows two terminal blocks used to connect the battery and limiting resistor to the 7-segment display. An extra block may be needed on TB1 to take all the cathode leads. Note that the 0.3in version of D1 fits into a 14-way IC holder.

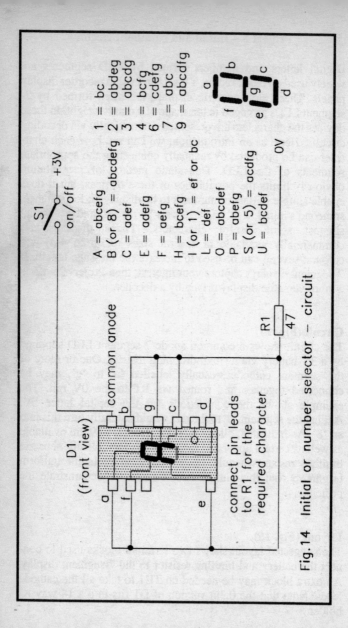

A = abcefg   1 = bc
B (or 8) = abcdefg   2 = abdeg
C = adef   3 = abcdg
E = adefg   4 = bcfg
F = aefg   6 = cdefg
H = bcefg   7 = abc
I (or 1) = ef or bc 9 = abcdfg
L = def
O = abcdef
P = abefg   S (or 5) = acdfg
U = bcdef

S1
on/off   +3V

0V

R1
47

D1
(front view)

common anode

a b g c d

a
f   b
  g
e   c
      d

f   e

connect pin leads
to R1 for the
required character

Fig.14 Initial or number selector – circuit

26

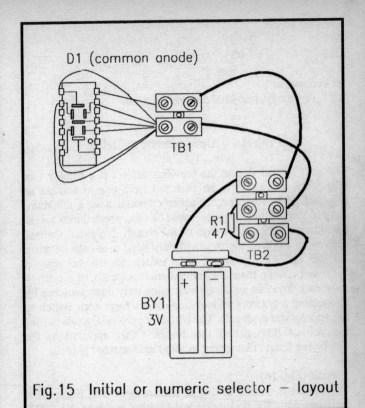

Fig.15 Initial or numeric selector — layout

Components for Project 5
(Figs. 14 & 15)

Resistor
R1   47

Semiconductor
D1   7-segment LED, common anode

Switch
S1   S.P.S.T. (on/off)

Terminal blocks
TB1   2-way
TB2   3-way

Miscellaneous
BY1 3V battery, insulated connecting wire.

Project 6 – Alphanumeric Switcher

The next logical step to the previous project is a display that
allows the characters to be switched from one to another as
required. In this version, all seven cathodes have a miniature
switch. Two of these projects could be incorporated into a desk
calendar to indicate the days of the month. Note that the one
displaying the tens digits would only need to switch between
'1', '2' and '3'. However, only switch S2 can be omitted
because between them these numbers require six of the seven
segments. You can get away with using only three switches by
connecting a network of isolating diodes from each switch to
the appropriate segments. The higher supply voltage allows for
the voltage drop across the diodes. Other applications for
displaying letters that spring to mind are for word games.

Circuit (Fig. 16)
The circuit is similar to that of the previous one, except that
switches S1 – S7, and individual limiting resistors, R1 – R7,
have been included in each of the LED cathode leads.

Layout (Fig. 17)
The exact layout will depend on the application, but the
diagram shows all the basic connections that have to be made.
Leads can be extended as necessary.

Components for Project 6
(Figs. 16 & 17)

Resistors
R1 – R7   1k (7 off)

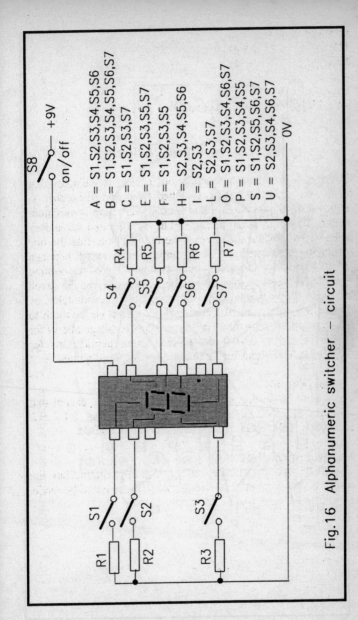

A = S1,S2,S3,S4,S5,S6
B = S1,S2,S3,S4,S5,S6,S7
C = S1,S2,S3,S7
E = S1,S2,S3,S5,S7
F = S1,S2,S3,S5
H = S2,S3,S4,S5,S6
I = S2,S3
L = S2,S3,S7
O = S1,S2,S3,S4,S6,S7
P = S1,S2,S3,S4,S5
S = S1,S2,S5,S6,S7
U = S2,S3,S4,S6,S7

Fig.16 Alphanumeric switcher — circuit

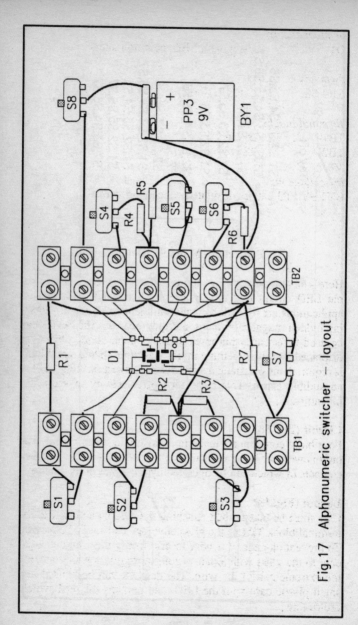

Fig.17 Alphanumeric switcher – layout

30

Semiconductor
D1   7-segment LED, common anode

Switches
S1 – S8   S.P.S.T. (8 off)

Terminal blocks
TB1   8-way
TB2   8-way

Miscellaneous
BY1 9V PP3 battery, insulated connecting wire.

Project 7 – Magnetic Detector

Here's an attractive project in more ways than one. It's a simple LED circuit that is activated by a magnet. Although its applications err towards the entertainment department – locating hidden magnets on maps and quiz boards – the device can be used for security purposes to detect open doors, objectives displaced, etc. If something more 'alarming' than a small LED is required, the magnetic detector could drive a flashing LED or an audible alarm. This basic idea offers plenty of scope for ingenuity.

Circuit (Fig. 18)
Four basic components make up this simple series circuit. The only newcomer is the glass magnetic reed switch RS1, the two contacts of which can be operated by a magnet in its vicinity.

Layout (Fig. 19)
Care must be taken when attaching the reed switch RS1 to the terminal block TB1 as the glass envelope can easily be broken. To prevent damage, it is wise to grip firmly the wire end adjacent to the glass with a pair of long-nose pliers while bending the extreme end of the wire. The detector can be housed in a small plastic case with the LED, and perhaps the reed switch, protruding.

31

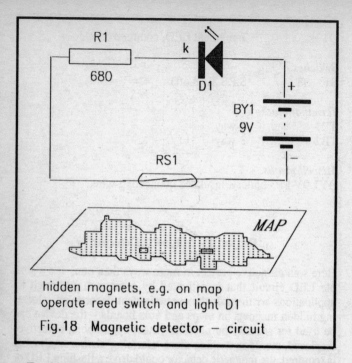

hidden magnets, e.g. on map
operate reed switch and light D1

Fig.18 Magnetic detector — circuit

For hidden treasure maps, especially large floor-type, the detector case could be mounted on the end of a stick, like the conventional metal detector. For security, the reed switch would need to be mounted in a door or window frame opposite the magnet and the LED or audible alarm extended to a remote monitoring position.

Components for Project 7
(Figs. 18 & 19)

Resistor
R1   680

Semiconductor
D1   LED (if flashing LED, omit R1)

Switch
RS1   magnetic reed switch

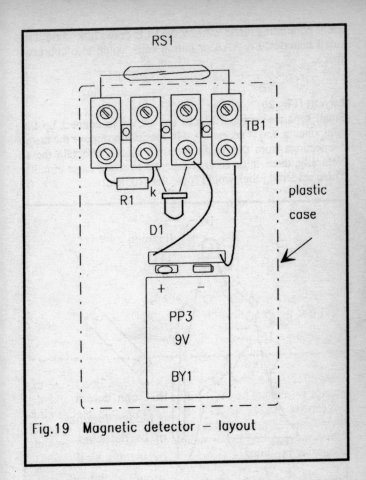

Fig.19   Magnetic detector — layout

Miscellaneous
BY1 9V PP3 battery with clip, plastic case, small magnets
behind maps or quiz cards, insulated connecting wire.

Project 8 – Mini-magnetic Detector

Some applications call for a really small magnetic detector and
the project can be reduced by using a flashing LED, which

needs no limiting resistor. At 3V the LED draws little current so small batteries, i.e. AAA or button cells, could also conserve space.

Layout (Fig. 20)

Small separate terminal blocks are shown to connect up the components, and if necessary, it is possible to remove the metal connections from the plastic terminal blocks to obtain these. Naturally, these must be kept separate to avoid short-circuits. Three soldered joints would solve the problem!

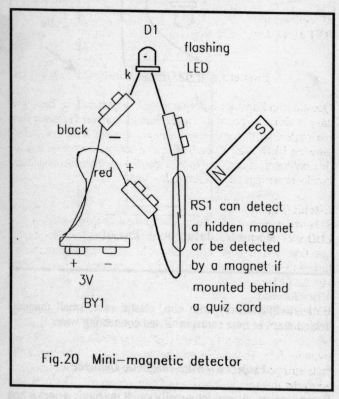

Fig.20   Mini—magnetic detector

Components for Project 8
(Fig. 20)

Semiconductor
D1   flashing LED

Switch
RS1   magnetic reed switch

Terminal blocks
miniature (3 off)

Miscellaneous
BY1 3V battery

Project 9 – Quiz Question Indicator

Question and answer quiz games are popular these days and
easy to devise – certainly easier than to answer! Here's a simple project to make that will reward correct answers with a
glowing LED. And if you like to find a more mundane use for
this indicator, it can double as a continuity tester to check for
breaks in wiring, check light bulbs, etc.

Circuit (Fig. 21)
This series circuit of a battery, a current-limiting resistor and
LED is completed when two probes are touched on the correct
question and answer terminals. The relevant terminals are
linked to achieve this, so providing a continuous circuit, causing the LED to glow.

Indicator Layout (Fig. 22)
The indicator layout shows a standard LED and limiting
resistor, but again a flashing LED is perhaps more effective
(without R1). The probes can be two insulated wires with the
ends stripped back, two commercial probes, or wires connected to the metallic points of used ballpoint pens. The indicator
layout may be free-standing or part of the quiz question TB
board layout.

Quiz Question TB Board Layout (Fig. 23)

This board consists of two terminal blocks mounted in parallel on a small plywood board. Two 4-way TBs are shown, but the number of 'ways' depends on the number of questions on the quiz card that covers the blocks. Holes in the card coincide with the screw terminals of the question and answer TBs. The card also serves to hide the links between the two TBs. Several quiz cards can be prepared as overlays, but as you will realise, players will remember the positions of the links after a while. You can change the links over occasionally or even reverse the board to ensure variation. Do make a note of the relevant combinations, otherwise there will be some peculiar answers!

A larger plywood quiz board can be made up for a social evening. Instead of terminal blocks, large drawing pins can be

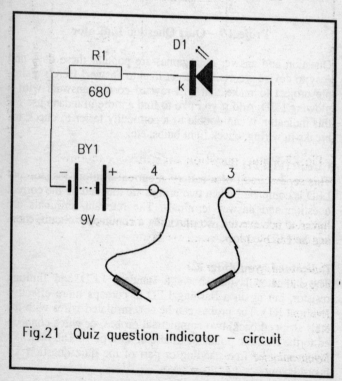

Fig.21 Quiz question indicator – circuit

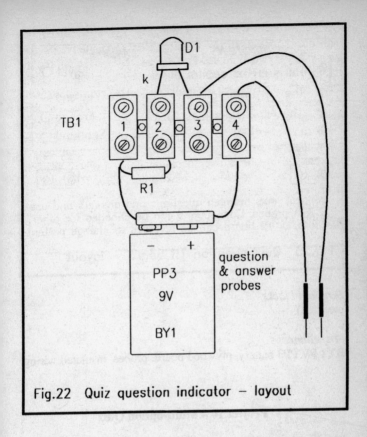

Fig.22 Quiz question indicator — layout

'pressed' into service with the links wire-wrapped around them and hidden by the quiz card overlay.

Components for Project 9
(Figs. 21 & 22)

Resistor
R1   680

Semiconductor
D1   LED (see text)

37

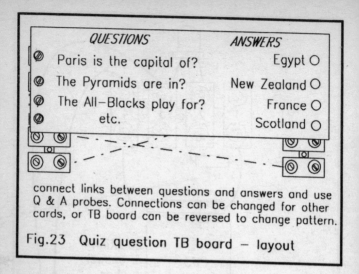

QUESTIONS | ANSWERS

Paris is the capital of? — Egypt ○

The Pyramids are in? — New Zealand ○

The All-Blacks play for? — France ○

etc. — Scotland ○

connect links between questions and answers and use
Q & A probes. Connections can be changed for other
cards, or TB board can be reversed to change pattern.

Fig.23 Quiz question TB board — layout

Terminal blocks
(see text)

Miscellaneous
BY1 9V PP3 battery, plywood board, probes, insulated wiring.

Project 10 – Multi-option Quiz

The multi-option quiz provides a variation on the previous
project using a green or red indication to confirm whether your
answers are correct or otherwise. Several questions and
answers can be prepared on quiz cards, depending on the
number of terminal blocks used. Only one probe is required for
the multiple answers.

Circuit (Fig. 24)

A tri-coloured LED D1 is used as the answer indicator. Resistor
R1 in the cathode lead limits the current. If preferred, D1 could
be replaced by a flashing red LED and a standard green LED.
The positive probe is touched on the terminal block (Fig. 26)

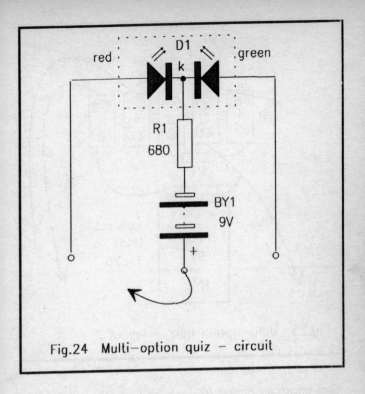

Fig.24 Multi—option quiz — circuit

but is effectively connected, depending on the contestant's decision, to either the red anode or the green anode.

Layout (Fig. 25)
The layout of the multi-option quiz circuit can be comfortably housed on a 5-way terminal block. As shown, the three flying leads are connected to the terminal block on the multi-option quiz card (Fig. 26). The green lead (G) and the red lead (R) are connected to the screw terminals denoting the correct and incorrect answers respectively.

As before, the quiz card is dimensioned to fit over the terminal block to cover the wiring links and to provide access for the probe to the screw terminals.

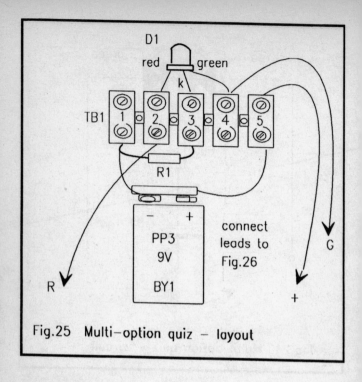

Fig.25 Multi-option quiz - layout

Components for Project 10
(Figs. 24, 25 & 26)

Resistor
R1   680

Semiconductor
D1   tri-coloured LED

Terminal blocks
TB1   5-way (2 off)

Miscellaneous
BY1 9V PP3 battery and clip, plywood base, probe, insulated
connecting wire.

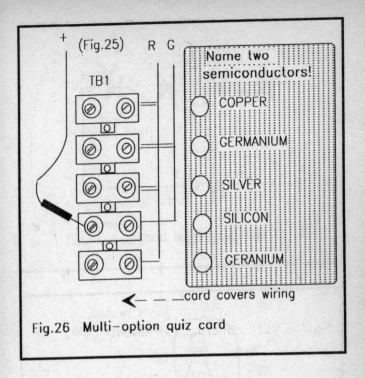

Fig.26 Multi-option quiz card

Project 11 – Flashing Lapel Badge

This simple project uses a different type of LED – the axial
LED. This is a miniature LED that looks like a tiny glass diode;
as with the diode, the cathode end is identified by a black band.
To make a really compact badge, the connections are best
soldered, but failing that, the connections can be covered by a
small piece of plastic, on which the LEDs can be mounted.

Circuit (Fig. 27)
The circuit consists of four LEDs, three axial LEDs and one
flashing LED, connected in series across a 9V battery. The
flashing LED D4 limits the current to less than 1mA in this
arrangement, ensuring long battery life. For this reason, and to

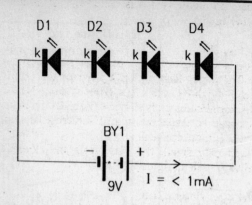

Fig.27 Flashing lapel badge – circuit

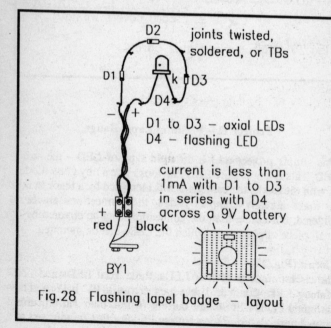

joints twisted, soldered, or TBs

D1 to D3 – axial LEDs
D4 – flashing LED

current is less than
1mA with D1 to D3
in series with D4
– across a 9V battery

Fig.28 Flashing lapel badge – layout

42

save space, no on/off switch is included, just disconnect the battery after use.

Layout (Fig. 28)
The layout shows one method of arranging the circuit components. The larger flashing LED provides the centre of the display with the three axial LEDs grouped around it. Although a two-way terminal block is shown to connect the battery clip, this block may be dispensed with if soldering or some other arrangement is more convenient.

Although only small, the glow from the axial LEDs is appreciable even in a brightly lit room.

Components for Project 11
(Figs. 27 & 28)

Semiconductors
D1 to D3   axial LED (3 off)
D4   flashing LED

Terminal block
see text

Miscellaneous
BY1 9V PP3 battery, plastic-covered flex.

Project 12 – Simple Light Meter

Finally, this section concludes with a project that measures light intensity. It uses a bridge circuit to measure the resistance of a light-dependent resistor and indicates this on a microammeter.

Circuit (Fig. 29)
The fixed resistors R1 and R2 form one half of the bridge, the light-dependent resistor PCC1 and the variable resistor VR1 forming the other half. When the ratio of R1/R2 is the same as the ratio PCC1/VR1 then the bridge is balanced and no current flows through M1. To set up the bridge, VR1 is adjusted at a

low light level for this null point. The meter then reads the intensity of light falling on PCC1.

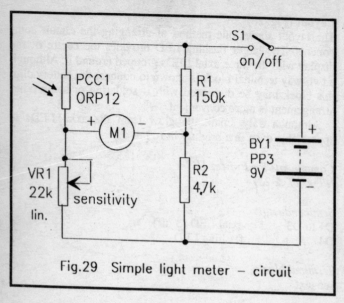

Fig.29 Simple light meter — circuit

Layout (Fig. 30)
The few components fit comfortably on the 6-way terminal block TB1. If a plastic case is used to house the meter and components, remember that PCC1 needs to be mounted externally so that it can 'see the light'.

Components for Project 12
(Figs. 29 & 30)

Resistors
R1   150k
R2   4.7k

Potentiometer
VR1   22k lin.

44

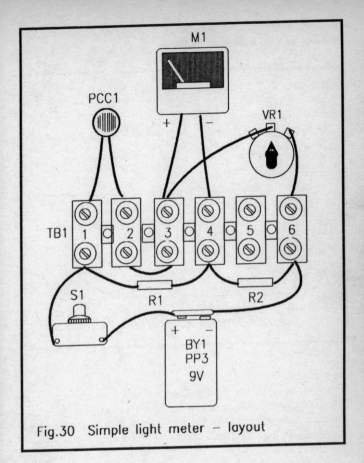

Fig.30   Simple light meter — layout

Meter
M1   250μA moving coil

Semiconductor
PCC1   ORP12

Switch
S1   S.P.S.T.

Miscellaneous
BY1 9V PP3 battery and clip, plastic case.

Chapter 4

TRANSISTOR OPTO-PROJECTS

The projects in this chapter include transistors, used mainly for switching purposes in these applications. Although in general a few more components are needed for these circuits, construction should present no difficulties if you have successfully completed the earlier projects. All transistors used in this book are npn types (see Fig. 4).

Project 13 – Monostable Pulse Stretcher

This project demonstrates how a monostable multivibrator can be used to increase the width of signal pulses. Why do we need to stretch pulses? There are several reasons. For instance, a switch contact does not always 'make' cleanly. It could produce some contact bounce resulting in spurious pulses in logic circuits. Extending the initial pulse slightly by means of a monostable means that any intermediate pulses are ignored. Trigger pulses of a standard width are useful for light-zapping games to give contestants equal opportunities and to prevent the trigger-happy spraying a target such as a light-dependent resistor. Another practical use for this circuit is as a variable time delay indicator for games.

Circuit (Fig. 31)

As the prefix "mono" suggests, the monostable remains in one stable state until it is triggered, assumes a different state and after a predetermined period reverts to the original state. Referring to the diagram, transistor TR1 is normally on, and consequently its collector is almost 0V. Via R2, this low collector voltage holds off TR2 by taking its base low. The electrolytic capacitor C1 in TR2 collector is discharged as both sides of it are at high potential. If the monostable is triggered by pushbutton S2, the short on TR1 base switches it off and its collector voltage rises. In turn, this switches on TR2 via R2. The short trigger pulse initiated by S2 also takes the –ve side of

47

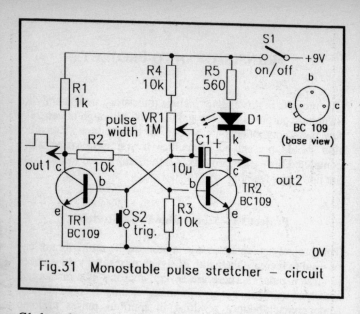

Fig.31 Monostable pulse stretcher – circuit

C1 low for a period determined by the time constant of C1 . (VR1 + R4). When the voltage on the base of TR1 is restored, TR1 switches on and TR2 switches off; i.e. the circuit reverts to its stable state. Turn VR1 to maximum to achieve maximum pulse width (D1 on for the longest period). If required, this period can be further increased by increasing the value of C1. Note that output pulses are available from both collectors in anti-phase. As it stands, the LED is on for the delay period. If preferred, the two collector load circuits can be interchanged (R1 for D1 + R5) so that D1 will be off during the unstable period and glow to indicate the end of it.

Layout (Fig. 32)

An 11-way terminal block TB1 is adequate to accommodate the monostable circuit and its supply. Make sure that the transistor leads comply with the base view and that the LED D1 and C1 are connected correctly. If this circuit is used as a simple timer, the pulse width control VR1 can be calibrated in seconds. Much longer delays are possible with monostables using CMOS gates as these have much higher impedances than transistors.

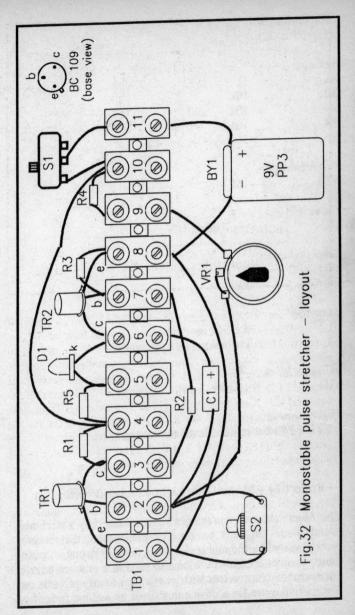

Fig.32 Monostable pulse stretcher – layout

49

Components for Project 13
(Figs. 31 & 32)

Resistors

R1	1k
R2	10k
R3	10k
R4	10k
R5	560

Potentiometer

VR1	1M

Capacitor

C1	10µF elect. 10V

Semiconductors

TR1, TR2	BC109 (2 off)
D1	LED

Switch

S1	S.P.S.T. (on/off)
S2	Pushbutton (non-locking)

Terminal block

TB1	11-way

Miscellaneous
BY1 9V PP3 battery, insulated connecting wire.

Project 14 – Morse Code Light Receiver/Practice Set

This Morse receiver senses light signals flashed by a torch and sounds them out on a buzzer. For this reason, the receiver works best when the ambient light is not too strong. A push-button enables the project to be also used as a practice buzzer. Furthermore, constructors with an eye for security projects can always find a use for a device that gives an audible indication

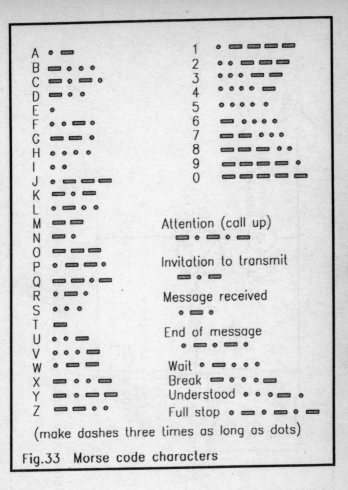

Fig.33 Morse code characters

(make dashes three times as long as dots)

when a light shines on it. Morse code characters are shown in Figure 33.

Circuit (Fig. 34)

To compensate for the ambient light, the sensitivity control VR1 is adjusted so that transistor TR1 is not conducting, i.e. the sounder WD1 is off. When a light is shone on to the light-

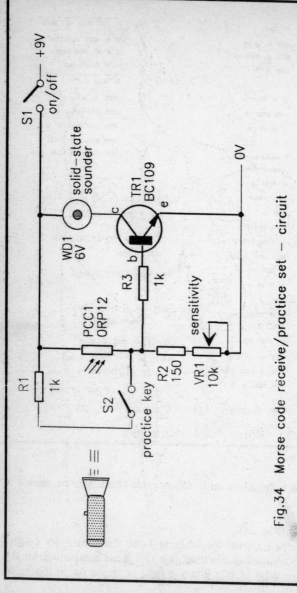

Fig.34 Morse code receive/practice set – circuit

52

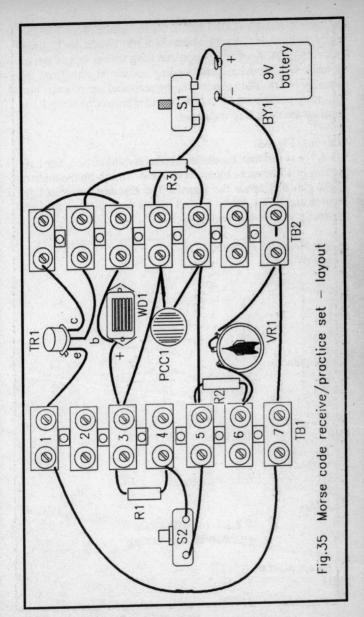

Fig.35 Morse code receive/practice set – layout

53

dependent resistor (LDR) PCC1, its resistance drops substantially and provides base current via R3 to switch on TR1 and activate WD1. A series of short and long flashes tapped out on a torch will produce corresponding audible signals from the sounder WD1. The sounder can be activated for practice purposes by pushbutton S2, which provides base current via R1 to operate the switching transistor.

Layout (Fig. 35)

Two 7-way terminal blocks are needed for this circuit. The light sensor PCC1 must be mounted in line-of-sight with the torch or light gun that sends the signals. The distance between light source and PCC1 can be several metres depending on the light intensity and the ambient light.

Components for Project 14
(Figs. 34 & 35)

Resistors

R1	1k
R2	150
R3	1k

Semiconductors

TR1	BC109
PCC1	ORP12

Potentiometer

VR1	10k lin.

Loudspeaker

WD1	solid-state buzzer

Switches

S1	S.P.S.T. (on-off)
S2	pushbutton, non-locking

Terminal blocks

TB1	7-way
TB2	7-way

BY1 9V PP3 battery and clip, insulated connecting wire.

Project 15 – Dual-light Target

This is a twin target for a simple light zapping game. A torch, or preferably a light gun with fixed length flashes is aimed at the targets. The sudden drop in the ohmic value of a light-depending resistance (LDR) when subjected to light causes the circuit to switch over the associated LEDs.

Circuit (Fig. 36)

As you would imagine, a bistable multivibrator has two stable states, i.e. it is stable in either the 'on' or the 'off' state. These flip-flop circuits can be used to sense input pulses, which cause the two outputs to change state (high to low, and vice versa) and to latch in that state until another trigger pulse is received.

If we assume TR1 is on, the collector is almost at 0V, D1 lights, and via R2 the base of TR2 is held low. Consequently

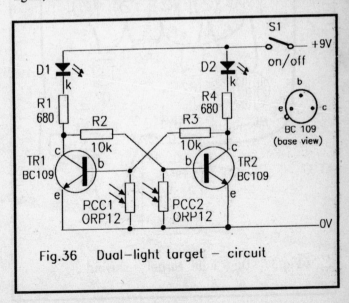

Fig.36   Dual-light target – circuit

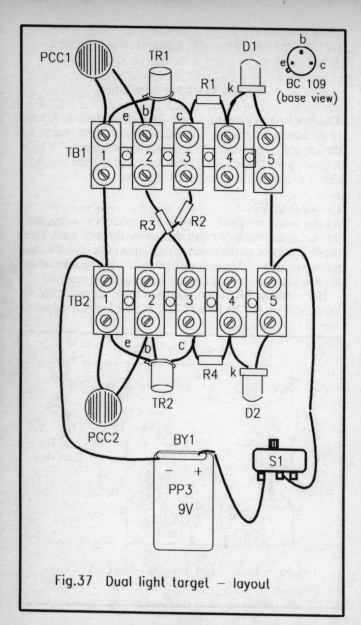

PCC1

TR1

D1

b
e · · c
BC 109
(base view)

R1

k

e   b   c

TB1   1   2   3   4   5

R3   R2

TB2   1   2   3   4   5

e   b   c

R4   k

PCC2

TR2

D2

BY1

−   +
PP3
9V

S1

Fig.37 Dual light target — layout

TR2 is switched off. This is one of the two stable states, i.e. TR1 on, TR2 off. Note that if a light is aimed at the LDR, PCC2, it will have no effect as the base of TR2 is already low. However, in this state, if PCC1 is exposed to light, its drop in resistance shorts the base of TR1 to 0V and switches it off. In turn, its collector voltage rises and via R2 turns on TR2. The drop in TR2 collector voltage lights D2 and via R3 also serves to hold TR1 off. This represents the other stable state, TR2 on, TR1 off. To change state, PCC2 must now be the target.

Layout (Fig. 37)
Two 5-way terminal blocks located in parallel appeared to be the best layout for this symmetrical circuit. The two targets could be conventional or more imaginative with the LEDs representing the eyes of some cartoon animal. The leads of the two target LDRs can be extended to allow more space so that the contestants have to re-aim after each successful shot.

Components for Project 15
(Figs. 36 & 37)

Resistors
R1, R4   680 (2 off)
R2, R3   10k (2 off)

Semiconductors
TR1, TR2   BC109 (2 off)
D1, D2   LED (2 off)
PCC1, PCC2   ORP12 (2 off)

Switch
S1   S.P.S.T. (on/off)

Terminal blocks
TB1, TB2   5-way (2 off)

Miscellaneous
BY1 9V PP3 battery and clip, insulated connecting wire.

Project 16 – Flip-flop Tumbler Trick

This is a flip-flop circuit similar to the previous one, but uses different sensing and indicating devices. A small magnet is hidden under the rim of a cardboard cup or held in the hand. Hey presto! When the cup is inverted over a cardboard saucer, an LED changes colour. The circuit has other uses besides this magic party trick. The magnetic reed switches can be mounted behind 'Yes/No' quiz cards to give a party or social evening that electronic flavour.

Circuit (Fig. 38)
The circuit operation is similar to that described in Project 15. Two magnetic reed switches RS1, RS2, are activated in turn by a small permanent magnet to switch over the flip-flop transistors TR1 and TR2. If RS1 is activated then TR1 is switched off, consequently, the green diode of D1 glows because the collector of TR1 is high, and TR2 switches on. Alternatively, if RS2

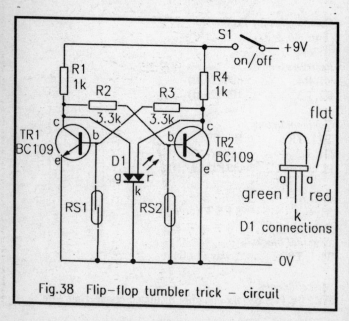

Fig.38 Flip-flop tumbler trick – circuit

58

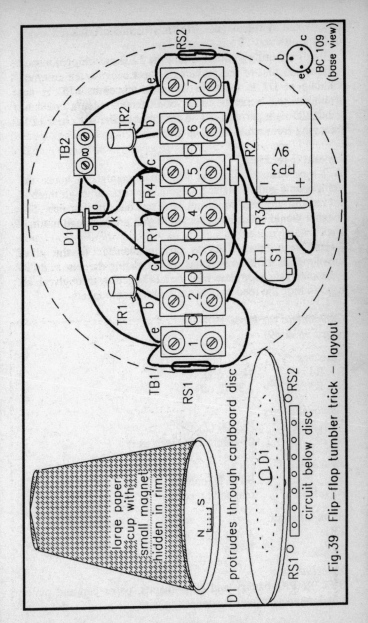

Fig.39 Flip–flop tumbler trick – layout

D1 protrudes through cardboard disc

circuit below disc

large paper
cup with
small magnet
hidden in rim

BC 109
(base view)

59

is activated by the magnet, TR2 is switched off, the red anode of D1 glows and TR1 is switched on.

It is interesting to observe that the LED switching action is different to that of the previous project because the common cathode of D1 is taken to 0V. If a tri-colour LED is not available, two separate LEDs of different colours could be used, although perhaps not so effective as the tri-colour LED changing from white to red or green.

Layout (Fig. 39)

A 7-way terminal block is just small enough to house the components and fit under a large paper cup, although there is no reason why this could not be a top hat, for instance. The magnet would be easier to secrete if you prefer to call it a hat-trick!

Use long nose pliers to prevent damage to the glass envelopes of the reed switches when bending the wire ends. A cardboard saucer or plate with the LED peeping through can be used to hide the reed switches and other components.

Components for Project 16
(Figs. 38 & 39)

Resistors
R1, R4   1k (2 off)
R2, R3   3.3k (2 off)

Semiconductors
TR1, TR2   BC109 (2 off)
D1   tri-colour LED (see text)

Switches
S1   S.P.S.T. (on/off)
RS1, RS2   magnetic reed switch (2 off)

Terminal block
TB1   7-way
TB2   1-way

Miscellaneous
BY1 9V PP3 battery and clip, magnet, paper cup and plate, small magnet, insulated connecting wire.

Project 17 – Dusk Detector

This simple circuit lights a 6-volt bulb when, as that old song says, 'When day is done and shadows fall … '. As you have probably guessed, this makes use of our old friend the light-dependent resistor. It could serve a useful function in a child's bedroom, automatically bringing a comforting glow when daylight fades, or when the main light is switched off.

Circuit (Fig. 40)
Variable resistor VR1 and the light-depending resistor PCC1 provide a potential divider to supply the base of the switching transistor TR1. In daylight, the resistance value of PCC1 will be relatively small so the slider of VR1 would need to be fairly low, i.e. more than 0.7V at the base for the transistor to switch on. If adjusting VR1 under daylight or artificial light conditions, increase the value of VR1 until the light LP1 goes off and then simulate dusk conditions by shading PCC1 to check whether LP1 comes on. Easier still, adjust VR1 at dusk to bring LP1 at the desired 'gloom' point. The resistor R1 limits the base current of TR1, which would otherwise be excessive if VR1 is rotated to its minimum resistance.

Layout (Fig. 41)
The few components needed for the dusk detector can easily be accommodated on a 6-way terminal block. The PCC1 always should be positioned where it can catch the ambient light. The switch and the lamp could be mounted on the top of a small plastic box. Make sure that lamp LP1 does not shine directly on PCC1 as there could be some interaction.

Components for Project 17
(Figs. 40 & 41)

Resistor
R1   1k

Potentiometer
VR1   10k lin.

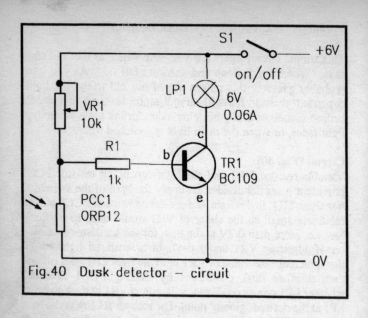

Fig.40 Dusk detector – circuit

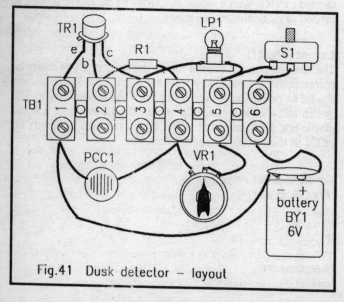

Fig.41 Dusk detector – layout

62

Semiconductors
TR1	BC 109
PCC1	ORP12

Lamp
LP1	6V 0.06A m.e.s. bulb

Switch
S1	S.P.S.T. (on/off)

Terminal block
TB1	6-way

Miscellaneous
BY1 6V battery and clip, lampholder, insulated connecting wire, container.

Project 18 – Economy Touch Switch

The applications for this economy touch switch range from a flashing security alarm, a visual door-push indication for the deaf, to a touch-contact game indicator. The operative word is economic as the quiescent battery current measured less than 5 micro-amps.

Circuit (Fig. 42)
Touch the two contacts and the electrolytic capacitor C1 on the base of TR1 charges from the positive rail through R1 to switch on the transistor. The emitter is direct-coupled to the base of TR2, which in turn switches on and activates the flashing LED D1 in its collector circuit. Even if the touch contact is momentary, the charge on C1 will hold the transistors in conduction for about 60 seconds during which D1 will flash.

Layout (Fig. 43)
A 7-way terminal block comfortably houses all components for this circuit. The touch contacts will possibly need a separate 2-way block depending on the particular application.

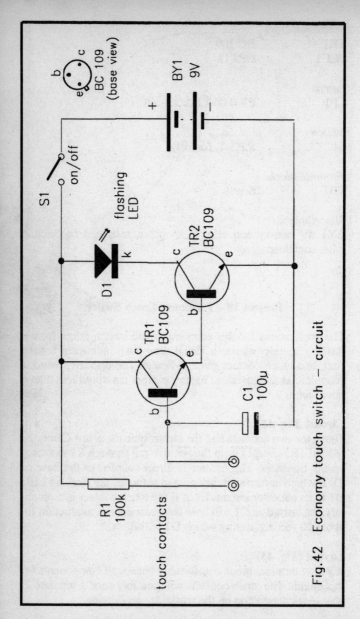

Fig.42 Economy touch switch – circuit

64

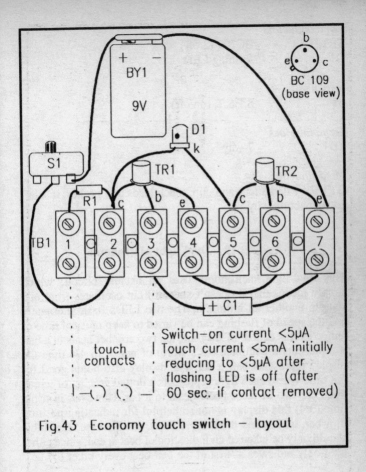

Fig.43 Economy touch switch — layout

Text within figure:

b
e · · c
BC 109
(base view)

+ BY1 −
9V

D1
k

S1

TR1

R1

TR2

c   b   e   c   b   e

TB1 1 2 3 4 5 6 7

+ C1

Switch−on current <5µA
Touch current <5mA initially
reducing to <5µA after
flashing LED is off (after
60 sec. if contact removed)

touch
contacts

Components for Project 18
(Figs. 42 & 43)

Resistor
R1   100k

Capacitor
C1   100µF 10V elect.

Semiconductors
TR1, TR2   BC109 (2 off)
D1   flashing LED

Switch
S1   S.P.S.T. (on/off)

Terminal block
TB1   7-way

Miscellaneous
BY1 9V PP3 battery and clip, touch leads and probes, insulated connecting wire.

Project 19 – Dual-light Metronome

This dual-light metronome uses an astable circuit, which simply means that it doesn't stay still but oscillates from one state to another ad infinitum. The two LEDs flash alternately and the speed of flashing can be varied to keep musical time or tempo as it is called. In 2/4 time, i.e. two crochet beats to a bar, it represents a complete bar's worth of notes. In 4/4 time the display represents half a bar. The display also holds good for 6/8 time where each light represents a dotted crochet of which there are two of these basic beats to a bar. However, in triple time (3/4) this display is not so helpful for indicating position in a bar, as 3/4 has three basic beats. In this case, the lights should only be taken as an indication of beat speed, since either light only indicates a 'first of the bar' beat every other bar.

Circuit (Fig. 44)

The two transistors, TR1 and TR2, are basically two identical amplifier stages that are cross-coupled capacitively so that they form an oscillator. The speed of oscillation can be calculated approximately from the balanced CR timing components between the transistor bases and the positive supply rail. If the speed range needs to be extended it can be increased by reducing the values of R2, R3 (or C1, C2) or the speed can be reduced by increasing the value of VR1 (or C1, C2).

66

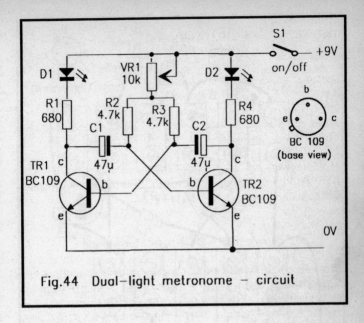

Fig.44   Dual—light metronome — circuit

Layout (Fig. 45)

The wiring of the two circuits on the parallel terminal blocks is almost identical, except that TB1 has an extra terminal (6) for the VR1 connections. Note that the positive ends of the capacitors C1, C2, should be connected to the collectors of the transistors. The scale of VR1 can be easily calibrated in beats per minute by counting the number of flashes against the second-hand of a watch. Sufficient accuracy should be obtained by counting over a period of half a minute and multiplying the count by two.

If a small plastic case is available, mount VR1 in the centre of the front panel with the two LEDs spaced apart. These should preferably be different colours so that the main (down) beat is readily distinguished.

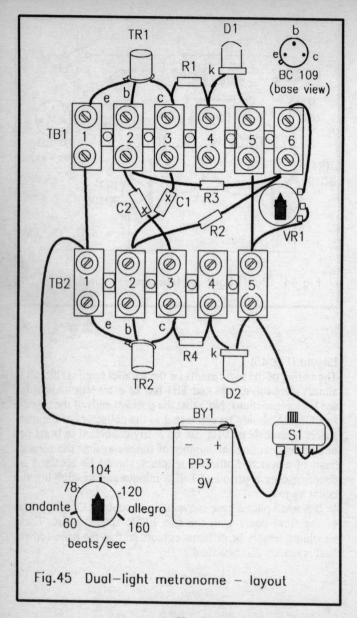

Fig.45 Dual—light metronome — layout

Components for Project 19
(Figs. 44 & 45)

Resistors
R1, R4   680 (2 off)
R2, R3   4.7k (2 off)

Capacitors
C1, C2   47μF 10V elect. (2 off)

Potentiometer
VR1   10k lin.

Semiconductors
TR1, TR2   BC109 (2 off)
D1, D2   LED (2 off)

Switch
S1   S.P.S.T. (on/off)

Terminal blocks
TB1   6-way
TB2   5-way

Miscellaneous
BY1 9V PP3 battery and clip, plastic box, insulated wiring.

Chapter 5

INTEGRATED CIRCUIT OPTO-DISPLAY PROJECTS

Newcomers to electronics may have dismissed any thought of building projects that include integrated circuits (ICs) because they appear to be too complicated. Perhaps it's the thought of all those transistors in a single chip that puts beginners off. Although internally they are complex electronic circuits, because the transistors, resistors, capacitors and other components are built-in, precisely selected and connected, the majority of the construction work has already been done. If you glance through some of the following IC circuit diagrams, you will see that in many cases only a few external components are necessary to build these versatile projects.

There are a few precautions to take when using ICs as they can be damaged by high-voltage static charges, although out of the thousands of chips handled by the author, out of the few that were faulty, none could be attributed to static. Plastics are one of the main generators of static charges so avoid wearing nylon when working with chips. Most CMOS (Complementary Metal-Oxide-Semiconductor) devices these days have internal protective diodes on their inputs, but it's wise to take one or two precautions when handling. Leave the device in its conductive foam wrapping until your circuit is built before inserting it in the holder. Never insert the IC into a holder with the supply connected and make sure it is fitted the right way round. If there are unused gates on an IC, it is best to connect all spare inputs to one of the supply lines to prevent them operating on static signals and consuming power.

Project 20 – Logic Probe

The flow of digital information in logic gates is generally by signals that are classified as 0 or 1 (low or high logic levels). The 0 is usually at, or near to, 0V. The 1 is a positive voltage, generally above 3 volts. This logic probe gives a visual indication of the logic levels in a digital circuit.

Circuit (Fig. 46)

The probe connections are connected to the input pin 7 of IC1a, one of the inverting buffers of a 4049. The output on pin 6 is connected to the anode of LED D2 and also to input pin 5 of another inverting buffer IC1b. The output on pin 4 is taken to the anode of LED D1. The cathodes of both D1 and D2 are routed via limiting resistor R1 to the 0V line.

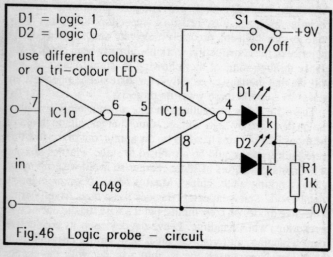

Fig.46   Logic probe – circuit

If the circuit under test is at logic 1, the probe input on pin 7 is inverted by gate IC1a to give a low output at pin 6. In turn, this is inverted by IC1b to produce a high output on pin 4, which lights D1 (logic 1 indicator).

However, if the circuit under test is at logic 0, the output of inverter IC1a, pin 6, will be high. As this output is also connected to the anode of D2, this LED (logic 0 indicator) will light. Note that as in this case, IC1b output is forced low, D1 does not light.

Summarising, a logic 1 signal gives a logic 1 on IC1b output to light D1, a logic 0 signal gives a logic 1 on IC1a output to light D2.

72

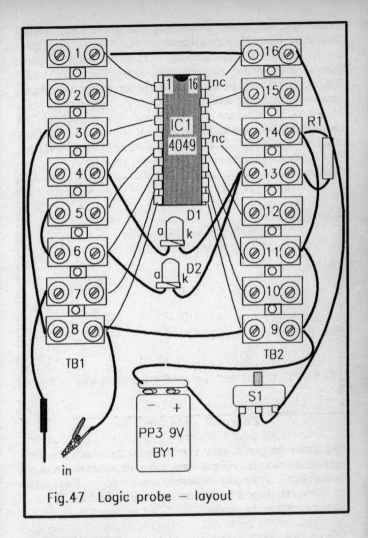

Fig.47 Logic probe — layout

Layout (Fig. 47)

A 16-way dual-in-line holder sandwiched between two 8-way terminal blocks provides all the necessary connections for this project. If this basic layout is prepared as a standard accessory on a plywood base, the circuit can easily be wired in a few minutes. As mentioned, if we regard the IC as a mysterious 'black box', the added components are few – only four in this circuit! Most of the wire links are to strap the inputs of spare gates to the 0V line to keep them quiet. The probe leads (TB1-7, TB1-8) can be terminated in prods or crocodile clips, whichever are most convenient.

Components for Project 20
(Figs. 46 & 47)

Resistor
R1   1k

Semiconductors
IC1   4049 Hex inverting buffer
D1, D2   LED (2 off, different colours)

Switch
S1   S.P.S.T. (on/off)

Terminal blocks
TB1, TB2   8-way (2 off)

Miscellaneous
BY1 9V PP3 battery and clip, probes, insulated wire.

Project 21 – Electronic Die

Sometimes the die is cast, but the result remains a mystery because it has rolled off the table. No more scrabbling around on the floor if you make up this electronic version. Just switch on, press a button and let the numbered LEDs do the rolling and release to freeze the result.

Circuit (Fig. 48)
On terminal block projects, where extra connections take up space, D7, a flashing LED is used instead of a timer IC to provide the clock input to a decade counter, IC1. When push-button S2 is pressed, D7 flashes at approximately twice per

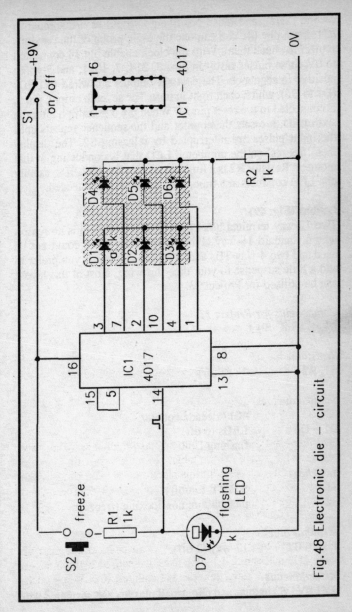

Fig.48 Electronic die – circuit

75

second (2Hz), and these positive-going pulses are applied to IC1, input pin 14. You can use the logic probe of the previous project to check them. With the clock enable pin 13 connected to 0V, these pulses result in pins 3, 2, 4, 7, 10, 1, and 5 going positive in sequence. The first six outputs are wired to LEDs (D1 to D6), which each light in turn. The seventh output, pin 5, is connected to the reset pin 15. When pin 5 goes high after the sixth LED, it resets the counter and the sequence repeats until the input pulses are interrupted by releasing S2. The display then 'freezes' on the numbered LED that is conducting at that moment. Resistor R2 is a limiting resistor for the LEDs; as only one LED conducts at a time, only one resistor is needed.

Layout (Fig. 49)
Two 12-way terminal blocks are shown, but there is no reason why a standard 16-way layout (two 8-way TBs) could not be used and two 4-way TBs added for the display. If you prefer to add a little suspense to your dice-throwing, most of this layout can be utilised for Project 23.

Components for Project 21
(Figs. 48 & 49)

Resistors
R1, R2   1k (2 off)

Semiconductors
IC1   4017 decade counter
D1 – D6   LEDs (6 off)
D7   flashing LED

Switches
S1   S.P.S.T. (on/off)
S2   pushbutton, non-locking (freeze)

Terminal blocks
TB1, TB2   12-way (2 off)

Miscellaneous
BY1 9V PP3 battery and clip, small plastic case, insulated wire.

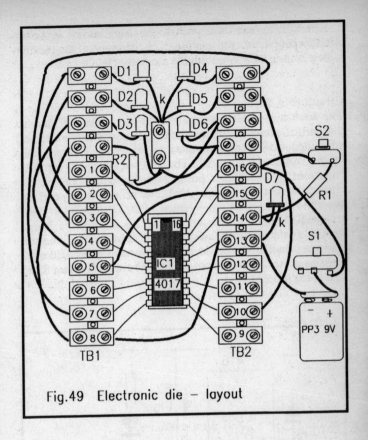

Fig.49 Electronic die – layout

Project 22 – Suspenseful Heads or Tails

You may have realised that a heads/tails circuit can be devised from the previous project by connecting the output of pin 4 of the counter IC1 to reset pin 15 instead of pin 5. You could of course dispense with LEDs D3 – D6, unless you want to make it a combined heads/tails and electronic die project. In that case, you would need to switch pin 15 to pin 4 or to pin 5 respectively.

However, to introduce a tantalizing delay into an either/or decision here is a suspenseful heads or tails project using a chip with a built-in voltage-controlled oscillator (VCO).

Circuit (Fig. 50)

The 4046 chip is described as a phase-locked loop IC, but in this particular application the circuit is confined to the voltage-controlled oscillator section. The frequency range is determined by the values of C1 and R1. The VCO input on IC1 pin 9 is controlled by the trigger pushbutton S2. When pressed, S2 charges the electrolytic capacitor C2 to the +9V supply and the squarewave output on pin 4 causes LEDs D1 and D2 to flash repeatedly in rapid succession. When S2 is released the charge on C2 gradually leaks away via R2, and as the potential decreases the flashing speed slows down until either D1 or D2 remains on to indicate heads or tails. Press and release S2 to repeat the process.

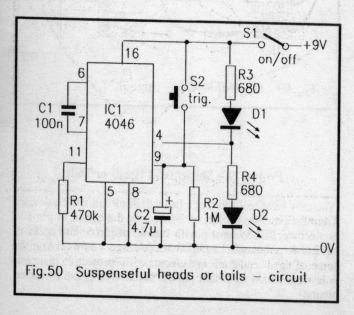

Fig.50 Suspenseful heads or tails — circuit

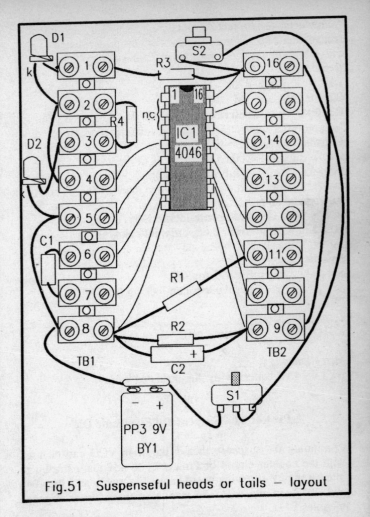

Fig.51 Suspenseful heads or tails — layout

Layout (Fig. 51)

A standard 16-way layout with two 8-way terminal blocks is sufficient to mount the components required for this circuit, as some of the IC pins are not connected. Choose two different coloured LEDs to make heads/tails identification more obvious.

Components for Project 22
(Figs. 50 & 51)

Resistors
R1   470k
R2   1M
R3, R4   680 (2 off)

Capacitors
C1   100n
C2   4.7µF 10V elect.

Semiconductors
IC1   4046 phase-locked loop
D1, D2   LED (2 off, different colours)

Switches
S1   S.P.S.T. (on/off)
S2   pushbutton, non-locking (trig.)

Terminal blocks
TB1, TB2   8-way (2 off)

Miscellaneous
BY1 9V PP3 battery with clip, insulated wiring.

Project 23 – Suspenseful Electronic Die

Continuing the suspense theme, the 4046 VCO can be used with the counter circuit of Project 21 to add that extra bit of interest in dice-throwing board games. As mentioned, the 4046 and 4017 circuits could be profitably made up as separate modules.

Circuit (Fig. 52)
As explained in the previous project, the 4046 is used purely as a VCO in this application. When pushbutton S2 is pressed the VCO input at IC1 pin 9 is taken to 9V and the fast pulses on output on pin 4 are applied to input pin 14 of the counter IC2.

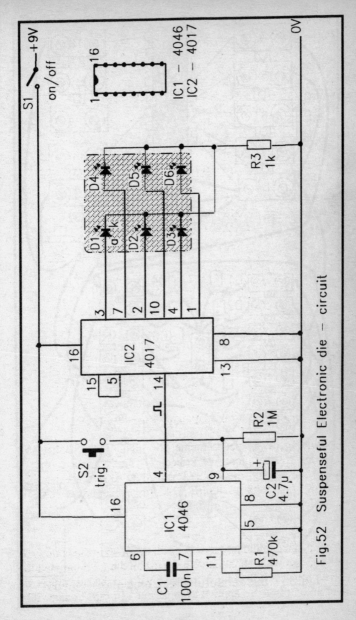

Fig.52 Suspenseful Electronic die – circuit

81

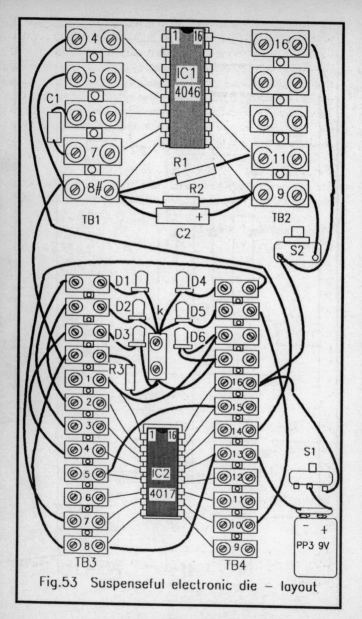

Fig.53 Suspenseful electronic die — layout

The counter section is identical to that described for Figure 48 in Project 21. The six outputs go high sequentially to activate LEDs D1 to D6 repeatedly at a fast rate. When S2 is released the input voltage to the VCO decreases gradually and the pulse rate to IC2 also decreases. Consequently, the flashing speed of the LEDs slows to a halt until eventually one LED remains on. This delay can be extended by increasing the value of C2; on the other hand, if you are impatient then substitute C2 for a small value to speed up the result.

Layout (Fig. 53)
The two modular layouts can be linked as shown. You may need an extra TB link to accommodate all the cathodes of the LEDs.

Components for Project 23
(Figs. 52 & 53)

Resistors
R1	470k
R2	1M
R3	1k

Capacitors
C1	100n
C2	4.7μF 10V elect. (see text)

Semiconductors
IC1	4046 phase-locked loop
IC2	4017 decade counter
D1 – D6	LEDs (6 off)

Switches
S1	S.P.S.T. (on/off)
S2	pushbutton, non-locking (freeze)

Terminal blocks
TB1, TB2	5-way (2 off)
TB3, TB4	12-way (2 off)

Miscellaneous
BY1 9V PP3 battery and clip, small plastic case, insulated wiring.

Project 24 – 'Light' Music

Rather like that old electronic instrument, the Theremin, this project is able, with a certain amount of skill, to pluck music out of thin air with the wave of the hand. In this circuit arrangement, the frequency of a voltage-controlled oscillator is varied by the amount of light that is allowed to fall on a light-dependent resistor. The result is some eerie sounds as the musical pitch changes.

Circuit (Fig. 54)

Once more the VCO of the 4046 IC is used to provide an audio oscillator that can be changed in frequency by varying the input voltage on IC1, pin 9. Musical notes are caused by regular vibrations of air, and all instruments must be made to vibrate to get the note underway, whether it's by hitting a drum, pressing a piano key, buzzing your lips into a mouthpiece or exercising your vocal cords. This oscillator has to be triggered by push-button S2 to initiate the sounds. The voltage on pin 9 will determine the pitch of the note, and in turn, this depends on the

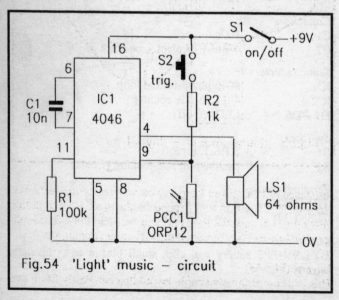

Fig.54 'Light' music – circuit

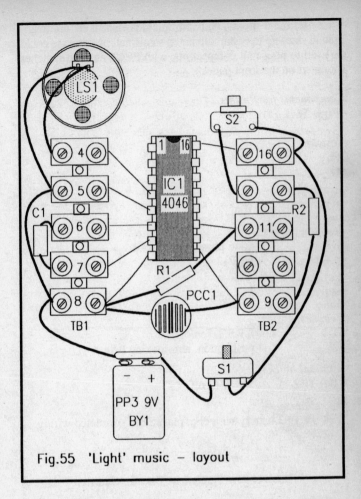

Fig.55 'Light' music — layout

resistance of PCC1. And I expect you've guessed that the resistance of PCC1 will in turn depend on the amount of light that falls on it, i.e. vary the light and you vary the tune! The loudspeaker LS1 can be connected directly to the output, pin 4.

Layout (Fig. 55)
This is a comparatively simple layout that can easily fit on two

5-way terminal blocks. Suitable miniature speakers are available in sizes up to 66mm diameter, so a small plastic case could be used to house all components, with PCC1 and the switches mounted on the front panel.

Components for Project 24
(Figs. 54 & 55)

Resistors
R1   100k
R2   1k

Capacitor
C1   10n

Semiconductors
IC1   4046 phase-locked loop
PCC1   ORP12

Loudspeaker
LS1   64 ohms

Switches
S1   S.P.S.T. (on/off)
S2   pushbutton, non-locking (trig.)

Terminal blocks
TB1, TB2   5-way (2 off)

Miscellaneous
BY1 9V PP3 battery with clip, plastic box, insulated wiring.

Project 25 – 7-segment Decade Counter

This project uses a flashing LED and a 4026 decade counter decoder to drive a 7-segment LED. Press and release a pushbutton to get a random number from 0 to 9. It demonstrates how a train of pulses can be counted and displayed by means of this decoder. Although this project is limited to a single decade (units), in practice several decoders can be cascaded to display tens, hundreds, etc.

Circuit (Fig. 56)

The input pulses produced by the flashing LED D1 are applied to the clock input, pin 1 of IC1. Pin 2 of IC1 is the clock inhibit input and blocks the clock pulses when it is held positive via R1. When pushbutton S2 is pressed, the 0V on pin 2 enables counting and the digits are displayed sequentially on the 7-segment LED D2. A single limiting resistor R3 is used in the common cathode lead of D2 in this simple circuit, but in practice limiting resistors should be fitted for all the segments to ensure constant intensity for all characters.

To cascade displays, the carry out pin 5 of the units display should be connected to the input pin 1 of the tens display, and so on. In practical circuits, the clock pulses are usually derived from a timer or a pulsing device.

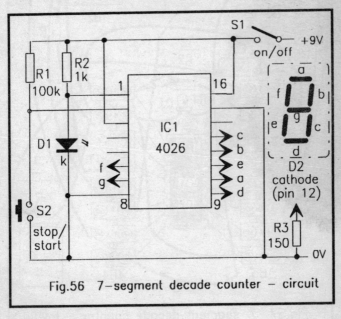

Fig.56   7-segment decade counter — circuit

Layout (Fig. 57)

The 0.3in 7-segment LED D2 fits into a 14-way dual-in-line IC holder, and requires two 4-way terminal blocks TB1, TB2, for its connections. Two 8-way terminal blocks, TB3, TB4, are needed for IC1 and the associated components.

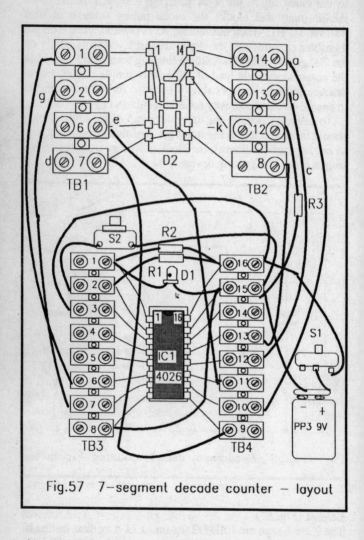

Fig.57   7—segment decade counter — layout

Components for Project 25
(Figs. 56 & 57

Resistors
R1   100k
R2   1k
R3   150

Semiconductors
IC1   4026 7-segment counter decoder
D1   flashing LED
D2   7-segment LED (common cathode)

Switches
S1   S.P.S.T. (on/off)
S2   pushbutton, non-locking (stop/start)

Terminal blocks
TB1, TB2   4-way (2 off)
TB3, TB4   8-way (2 off)

Miscellaneous
BY1 9V PP3 battery and clip.

Project 26 – Category Select Game

This project is based on a flashing LED clocking a counter, but this time all the outputs of the decade counter are displayed in sequence to select, at random, ten categories for a quiz game.

Circuit (Fig. 58)
The freeze pushbutton S2 is pressed to energise the flashing LED D6, which applies pulses at about two per second to the clock input, pin 14 of counter IC1. This causes the ten outputs to produce a sequence positive pulse repetitively until S2 is released. At this instant, the output that is being pulsed remains high and its associated LED remains on. All ten outputs could each have a standard LED, but for this application D1 to D5

89

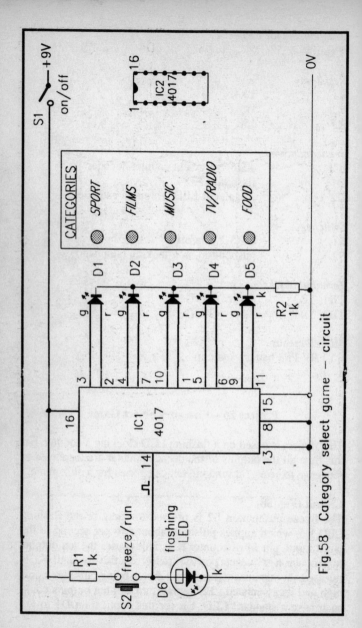

Fig.58 Category select game — circuit

90

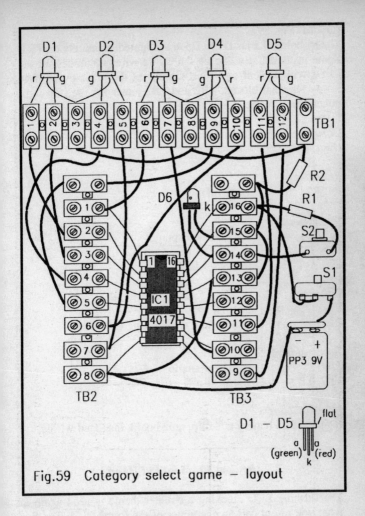

Fig.59 Category select game — layout

are tri-colour LEDs, displaying red or green. The two colours can represent a particular aspect of the category, or which team gets the question, or the list can be extended to ten categories. As only one LED is energised at a time, a common current-limiting resistor R2 is sufficient.

Layout (Fig. 59)

The tri-colour LEDs D1 to D5 are mounted separately on TB1. Some insulated sleeving on the centre wires (cathodes) of the LEDs will prevent any short-circuits at the cross-overs. Two 9-way terminal blocks, TB2 and TB3, cater for the IC1 components and connections.

Components for Project 26
(Figs. 58 & 59)

Resistors
R1, R2   1k (2 off)

Semiconductors
IC1   4017 decade counter
D1 – D5   tri-colour LED (5 off)
D6   flashing LED

Switches
S1   S.P.S.T. (on/off)
S2   pushbutton, non-locking (freeze/run)

Terminal blocks
TB1   12-way + single
TB2, TB3   9-way (2 off)

Miscellaneous
BY1 9V PP3 battery and clip, quiz board, insulated wiring.

Project 27 – Light of Hand

The flashing LED clocking a counter theme is used again in what you might call an encounter of the fourth kind. The five tri-colour LED display is also identical to the previous project, but there is an important difference in the way the circuit is pulsed. The project is an update of the age-old party game where steadiness of hand is tested by trying to pass a loop over a bent wire frame without ringing alarm bells. The bells are replaced here by a LED scoreboard.

92

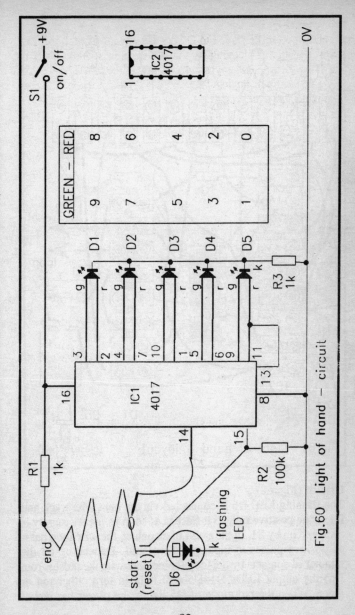

Fig.60 Light of hand — circuit

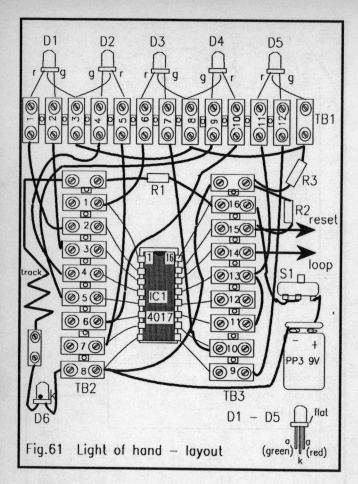

Fig.61 Light of hand – layout

D1 – D5

(green) a | a (red)
k

Circuit (Fig. 60)

The flashing LED D6 is connected via the bent wire track and R1 to the positive rail, so it flashes as soon as the 9V supply is switched on by S1. In the event of a contact, the wire loop passes positive pulses to input pin 14 of IC1. Depending on the number of contacts by the loop (coincident with the pulses from D6) the output LEDs D1–D5 will light in turn either red or green. When the red diode of D5 lights, the player has had at

94

least 10 contacts and has therefore scored zero. In this position, output pin 11 is high and as it is directly coupled to the clock enable pin 13 further pulses have no effect as the clock is now disabled. However, by returning the loop back to the start of the wire it short-circuits the reset pin 15 to the positive end of D6 and provide a reset pulse to restart the game.

Layout (Fig. 61)
The layout is very similar to the previous project, but there is an extra resistor to wire in and some extra links and the wire loop to take care of. Use some fairly stout cable for the bent wire; metal coathangers have been bent to good effect in the past, and as there are nine lives to lose on this game, why not make it in the shape of a cat?

Components for Project 27
(Figs. 60 & 61)

Resistors
| R1, R3 | 1k (2 off) |
| R2 | 100k |

Semiconductors
IC1	4017 decade counter
D1 – D5	tri-colour LEDs (5 off)
D6	flashing LED

Switch
| S1 | S.P.S.T. (on/off) |

Terminal blocks
| TB1 | 12-way + 2 singles |
| TB2, TB3 | 9-way (2 off) |

Miscellaneous
BY1 9V PP3 battery and clip, insulated wiring.

Project 28 – General-purpose Timer

The popular 555 timer IC is wired in the monostable mode to provide this general-purpose timer. The delay period before the LED comes on can be varied manually up to about 15 minutes, but can be extended still further by increasing the values of the timing components.

Circuit (Fig. 62)
At switch-on a pulse is applied to the trigger input pin 2, which allows C1 to charge through R1 and VR1. When the charge on C1 is 66% of the supply voltage, it is discharged and the output on pin 3 goes low and D1 is energised. The delay period before D1 comes on is determined by the values of C1, R1 and VR1.

Layout (Fig. 63)
The 8-pin timer IC1 and its few components need only two 5-way terminal blocks and can be wired in a few minutes. This has many uses from games to more homely reminders to switch things on or off as the case may be. It certainly deserves a project box.

Components for Project 28
(Figs. 62 & 63)

Resistors
R1   1k
R2   22k

Capacitors
C1   470μF 10V elect.
C2   10nF
C3   100nF

Potentiometer
VR1   1M lin.

Semiconductors
IC1   555 timer
D1   LED (standard or flashing)

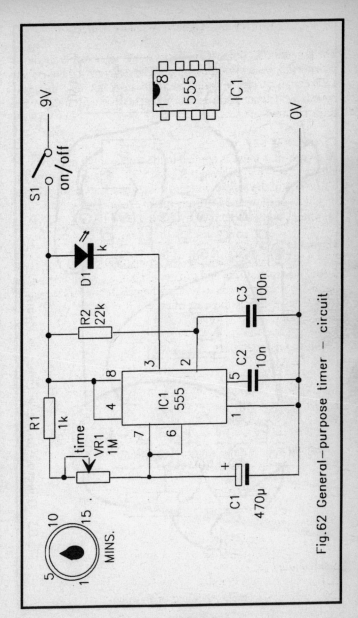

Fig.62 General—purpose timer — circuit

97

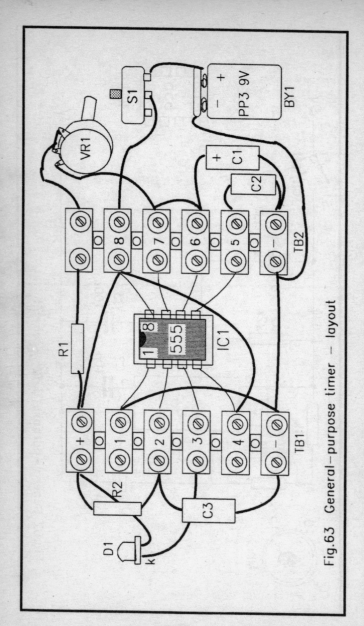

Fig.63 General-purpose timer — layout

98

Project 29 – Touch Delay Lamp

A light that can be easily switched on for a few seconds
and switches off automatically can find a number of useful
applications from improving safety in dimly-lit areas to
security monitoring.

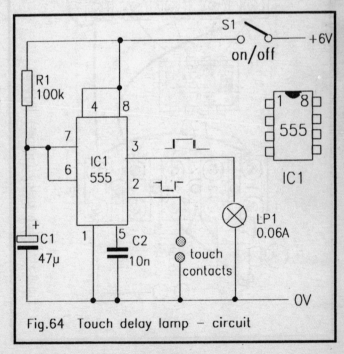

Fig.64   Touch delay lamp — circuit

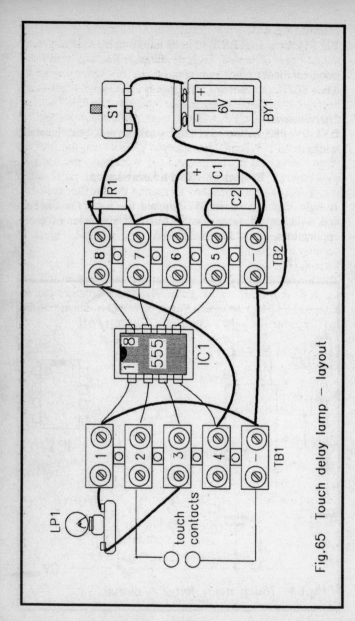

Fig.65 Touch delay lamp – layout

Circuit (Fig. 64)

The 555 timer is again used in its monostable mode to give an output pulse of several seconds duration that will energise a small 6V lamp. When two contacts are bridged, even by the touch of a finger, the skin resistance is low enough to provide a negative-going input to the trigger input pin 2 of IC1. The electrolytic capacitor C1 is allowed to charge through R1 and for the few seconds while it is charging, output pin 3 goes high and brings on LP1. When C1 has charged to about two-thirds of the supply voltage it discharges and the voltage on pin 3 drops, switching off LP1. As previously mentioned, the pulse width can be increased if desired by increasing the CR time constant. The 6V supply uses four 1.5V AA cells in a battery box as LP1 is a 6V lamp drawing 60mA. Alternatively, a long-life 6V lighting battery could be substituted.

Layout (Fig. 65)

Two 5-way terminal blocks are all that are required for IC1 and the few associated components. The touch contacts can be extended by a length of twin flex to be in a convenient position for triggering the light circuit.

Components for Project 29
(Figs. 64 & 65)

Resistor
R1   100k

Capacitors
C1   47μF 10V elect.
C2   10nF

Semiconductor
IC1   555 timer

Lamp
LP1   6V 0.06A m.e.s. bulb and holder

Switch
S1   S.P.S.T. (on/off)

Terminal blocks
TB1, TB2   5-way (2 off)

Miscellaneous
BY1 6V battery, insulated wiring.

Project 30 – Light and Latch Display

You must admit that a quadruple D-latch in your Christmas stocking may not be your idea of fun, but even a latch can have its lighter moments. You can use a magic wand to light four LEDs, mounted on a small display Christmas tree for instance, and latch them on if you are quick enough. You will find it is a bit like trying to spin plates on a TV show; while you get one spinning, there are others that are about to stop and fall off. There are only four LEDs to light in a limited time, but some remain on for only a few seconds. The secret is to light them in the right order so that you can latch them on before any go off. Of course, you don't tell your guests this when they have a go!

Circuit (Fig. 66)
Positive input pulses on any of the four data inputs, pins 4, 7, 13, 14 of IC1 produce positive signals on the four buffered outputs, pins 2, 10, 11, 1 respectively. In this case, the positive pulses are obtained by touching the inputs with a probe connected to the +9V supply rail. An electrolytic capacitor (C1–C4) connected to each input is charged by the probe and produces a signal on the output, which lights the relevant LED. However, each input electrolytic capacitor is slowly discharged by a bridging resistor. As the input voltage charge fades, so does the output LED unless the latch switch S2 is closed before that happens. Although the input capacitors all have the same value, the four discharge resistors, R1 to R4, are all different. For instance, resistor R4 has the smallest value, so a charge on input pin 14 will light D4 for only a few seconds. Better to leave this one until last, otherwise it will be out before you flick the latch switch!

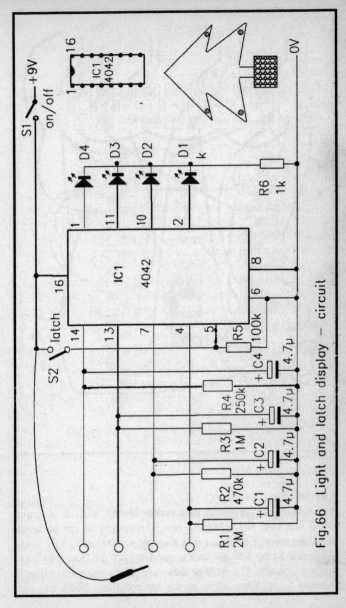

Fig.66 Light and latch display — circuit

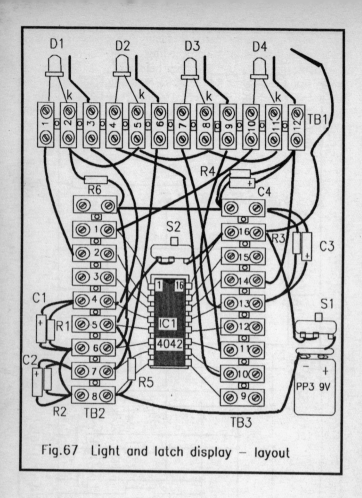

Fig.67 Light and latch display — layout

Layout (Fig. 67)

This circuit is a bit greedy on terminal blocks, and one is tempt-
ed to reach for the soldering iron. Depending on the presentation, the small Christmas tree display, for instance, TB1 could
be divided into 3-way blocks, one for each LED and its input
trigger contact. The further these are apart, the more effort is
needed to get them all lit in the limited time. If it's too easy

then, as you probably realise, reducing the values of the input resistors will speed up the proceedings.

Enable pins 5 and 6 are both held low with S2 open, so signals on the outputs follow those on the inputs until latched by a positive on pin 5 via S2. However, the circuit could be latched for a limited time by simply connecting a large value electrolytic capacitor in place of R5 and replacing S2 by a contact as in the case of the four inputs. The circuit would then be latched by touching the probe on to this contact last.

Components for Project 30
(Figs. 66 & 67)

Resistors

R1	2M
R2	470k
R3	1M
R4	250k
R5	100k
R6	1k

Capacitors

C1 – C4	4.7µF 10V elect. (4 off)

Semiconductors

IC1	4042 quadruple D-latch
D1 – D4	LED (4 off)

Switches

S1	S.P.S.T. (on/off)
S2	S.P.S.T. (latch)

Terminal blocks

TB1	12-way
TB2, TB3	9-way (2 off)

Miscellaneous
BY1 9V PP3 battery and clip, probe and contacts, insulated wiring.

Project 31 – Multi-choice Timer

A 14-stage binary timer offers plenty of choice for making things happen over short or long intervals, in display models for instance. More seriously, it could form the basis for a security system where lights can be arranged to come on over various intervals of time to give prowlers the impression that the premises are occupied.

Circuit (Fig. 68)
Once again, the flashing LED is used as the clock for input to pin 10 of IC1. The input of approximately 2Hz gives output off/on periods from about 1s to 2 hours with ten intermediate outputs available as shown. Two LED indicator circuits are shown, but more can be added. The outputs can be used to drive the bases of switching transistors to energise lamps, or relays if necessary. The reset, pin 11, can be connected to any of the outputs to restart the counter timing sequence from a particular point in time.

For even longer timing sequences, D1 can be replaced by a timer, such as the 555, wired in the astable mode.

Layout (Fig. 69)
The layout shows the timer with two LEDs available for connection to any of the twelve available outputs. Refer to the circuit diagram Figure 68 for the TB connections for various on/off periods. Additional terminal blocks may be necessary for some applications.

Components for Project 31
(Figs. 68 & 69)

Resistors
R1 – R3   1k (3 off) (see text)

Semiconductors
IC1   4020 14-stage binary counter
D1   flashing LED
D2, D3   LED (2 off) (see text)

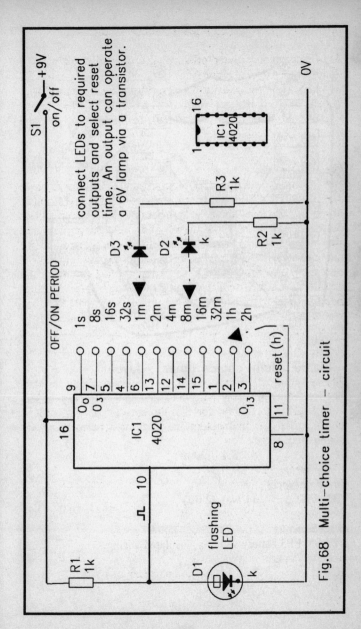

Fig.68 Multi–choice timer – circuit

107

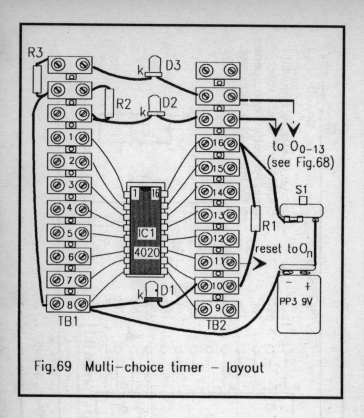

Fig.69 Multi–choice timer – layout

Switch
S1   S.P.S.T. (on/off)

Terminal blocks
TB1, TB2   11-way (2 off)

Miscellaneous
BY1 9V PP3 battery and clip, insulated wiring.

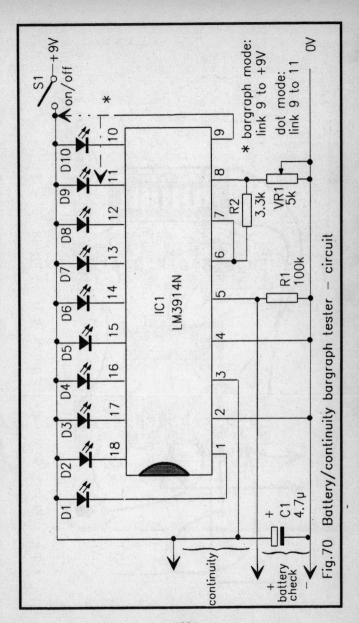

Fig.70 Battery/continuity bargraph tester – circuit

109

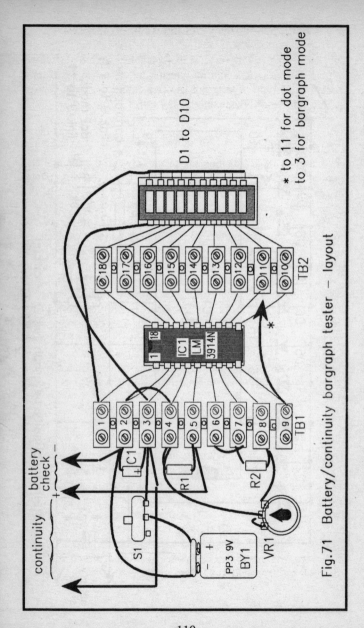

Fig.71   Battery/continuity bargraph tester – layout

* to 11 for dot mode
  to 3 for bargraph mode

110

Project 32 – Battery/Continuity Bargraph Tester

This LED display driver LM3914 can be used to test low-voltage batteries, as a continuity tester, or to measure moisture content. This type of bargraph is often found in music centres and amplifiers to indicate signal strength.

Circuit (Fig. 70)

The battery voltage readings are taken between the 0V line and a probe connected to input pin 5 of IC1. The reference voltage on pin 8 can be set by the sensitivity control VR1, part of the potential divider chain VR1, R2 from the high reference, pin 6.

The continuity readings are taken between pin 5 and the positive supply voltage on pin 3. A high resistor of 100k or more can be inserted in the probe lead if readings are too high, i.e. if most of the LED segments are on.

If a PP3 battery is used, it is better to connect the display in the dot mode, i.e. only one LED segment on at a time, to conserve energy. Connect the link between pin 9 and pin 11 for the dot mode. In the bargraph mode, the LED segments light progressively as the input increases to give a strip of light. As each LED segment draws a current of about 10mA a bigger capacity battery such as the PP9 is advised. Connect the link between pin 9 and the +9V rail (pin 3) for bargraph mode operation.

Layout (Fig. 71)

Two 9-way terminal blocks are necessary to provide connections for the 18-way display driver chip. Commercial 18-pin dual-in-line holders are available, but you could get by with using two IC holders end to end. Alternatively, you could use a 16-way holder and make do with a bargraph of eight LEDs omitting two LED sections (on pins 1 and 18). As shown a bargraph LED is used as an option to ten separate LEDs. This, or its holder, will need short flexible leads soldered to it with a common positive lead to all the anodes.

111

Components for Project 32
(Figs. 70 & 71)

Resistors
R1   100k
R2   3.3k

Capacitor
C1   4.7µF 10V elect.

Potentiometer
VR1   5k lin.

Semiconductors
IC1   LM3914N LED-display driver
D1 – D10   bargraph display or ten separate LEDs

Switch
S1   S.P.S.T. (on/off)

Terminal blocks
TB1, TB2   9-way (2 off)

Miscellaneous
BY1 9V battery and clip (see text), probes, insulated wiring.

Project 33 – Team Totaliser

The dual 4-input NAND gate adds its quota of entertainment in this Team Totaliser project. In team or party games, with all the rush and excitement it is often difficult to work out whether all contestants in each team have run, hopped, popped a balloon or whatever to complete their turn. The answer is to get each contestant to make a contact with a probe before handing over to the next person on the team. The electronic totaliser will add up the number of contestants successfully competing and indicate the first team home – red or green! You can probably think of other interesting applications for this circuit; an 8-input NAND

112

gate (4068) is available in the 4000 series if you want to extend this idea.

Circuit (Fig. 72)

With the circuit switched on, and no contact made with the probe attached to R1 as shown in the diagram, all inputs of the

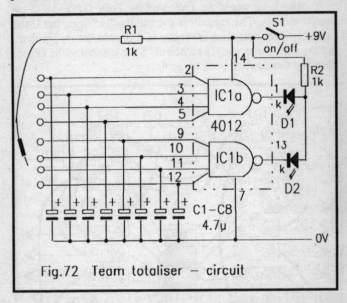

Fig.72 Team totaliser – circuit

two NAND gates IC1a and IC1b are held low (logic 0) by the electrolytic capacitors C1 to C8 connected to 0V. Consequently, both outputs of the NAND gates (pin 1 and pin 13) are at logic 1 and both LEDs D1 and D2 are off. Consider the inputs to IC1a. If the probe is touched on the input contact to C1 momentarily, the capacitor receives a charge from the +9V rail via R1 and a logic 1 is applied to input pin 2. However, this has no immediate effect on the circuit as the condition for switching a NAND gate output to logic 0 is that all four inputs must be at logic 1. When the contacts to C1, C2, C3 and C4 are touched by the probe, the capacitors charge and all four inputs of IC 1a (pins 2, 3, 4, 5) are at logic 1. Consequently, output pin 1 is forced to logic 0 and D1 (a red LED) lights via the limiter R2.

This assumes that NAND gate IC1a inputs and output are allocated to the red team. If all four inputs capacitors C5, C6, C7 and C8 were charged first by the probe, then the four inputs of IC1b (pins 9, 10, 11, 12) would be at logic 1 and output pin 13 would be switched to logic 0 and D2 would light, denoting a green victory.

A dead heat would be indicated by both D1 and D2 on simultaneously. The capacitors eventually discharge, but if the game lasts no more than ten minutes this presents no problem. For the next game, simply switch off S1 to discharge the capacitors and then switch back on again.

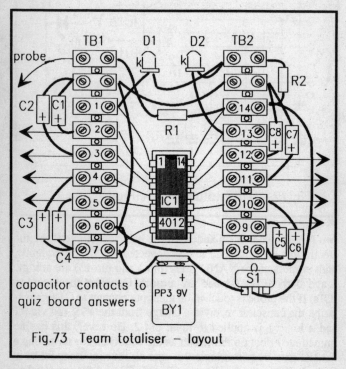

Fig.73 Team totaliser – layout

Layout (Fig. 73)
Miniature slider switches were originally planned to do the input switching, but for this simple application, the capacitors

provided a much neater solution, especially when terminal blocks are the order of the day. The 4012 IC requires 14 terminals so two 9-way terminal blocks are used. As the two teams are allocated four contacts each, the two groups will need to be spaced apart; extend the four-way cables as necessary. The contacts can take various forms depending on the application and ingenuity of the constructor. To add interest, you can make contestants work for their points. Contacts can be deliberately a little inaccessible, and some skill may be required. For instance, the probe, or better still two probes, could be 'electronic fishing rods' dangled over 'electric eels' (contacts connected to the capacitors), etc.

Components for Project 33
(Figs. 72 & 73)

Resistors
R1, R2   1k (2 off)

Capacitors
C1 – C8   4.7µF (8 off)

Semiconductors
IC1   4012 dual 4-input NAND gate
D1, D2   LED (2 off)

Switch
S1   S.P.S.T. (on/off)

Miscellaneous
BY1 9V PP3 battery with clip, probes, insulated wiring.

Project 34 – Select Four Quiz

The dual 4-input NAND gate chip circuit can be extended to make an interesting quiz game. Out of eight possible answers to a question, a contestant has to select the four correct ones in a given time. Only a maximum of four answer switches must be

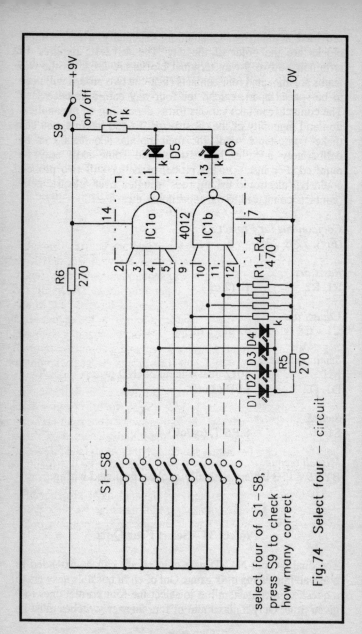

Fig.74 Select four — circuit

select four of S1—S8,
press S9 to check
how many correct

116

on at a time. If the four are correct then a green LED will indicate success. Otherwise, the contestant must switch off the answer, or answers, thought to be wrong and switch on others in their place. But remember, no more than a total of four must be on. The game is reminiscent of the TV quiz game show called 'Wipeout'.

Also here, to maintain interest, after each switching attempt the circuit is switched on to reveal the number of correct answers (but not which ones!). The contestant must keep switch selecting and testing until time is up, or the four correct answers are switched to light the green LED indicator. Get four incorrect answers and the red light indicates dismal failure.

Circuit (Fig. 74)

In this circuit, the NAND gates inputs are held low initially; IC1a inputs by D1 to D4 (test) in series with R5, and IC1b inputs by resistors R1 to R4. Consequently, the outputs (pins 1 and 13) are high and the two output indicator LEDs D5 and D6 do not conduct. All four switches S1 to S4 have to be selected, i.e. all inputs at logic 1 to produce a logic 0 at the output pin 1 to bring the correct answer LED, D5 on. Conversely, switches S5 to S8 represent the wrong answers and a combination of all four giving a logic 1 on each of IC1b inputs via R6 will produce a logic 0 on output pin 13 to bring on the unlucky LED, D6.

The playing procedure is to select the chosen four switches from S1–S8 with the on/off switch S9 in the off position. Turn S9 on to observe whether all four answers were right (D5 on), or to see from D1–D4 what was the initial success. These four test LEDs can be either standard types or axial LEDs, and should be grouped as a separate display to make it difficult to discover which of the chosen answers were correct.

The switch leads to the control panel must also be interchanged to match different answer patterns on quiz cards, otherwise players will tend to memorise the position of the switches.

Indicator Layout (Fig. 75)

For convenience, the layout has been drawn separately for the control panel and the indicator, whereas the circuit diagram

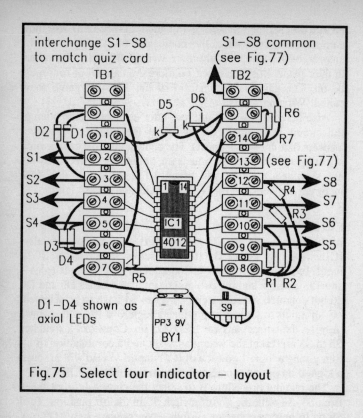

interchange S1–S8 to match quiz card

S1–S8 common (see Fig.77)

Fig.75 Select four indicator — layout

shows both sections. The 4012 dual 4-input NAND gate requires 14 connections; two 9-way terminal blocks take care of the six LEDs and seven resistors. Although switch positions are specified for the flying leads, they would of course be interchanged depending on the answer layout of a particular quiz card; a typical example is shown in Figure 76.

Control Panel Layout (Fig. 77)
The final layout of the control panel will determine the size and shape of the quiz card (Fig. 76). Preferably, the switches should be mounted equidistantly on a plywood base as shown. Two 8-way terminal blocks should suffice for the switch connections, and a suggested layout is shown. The TBs should be easily

accessible in order to ring the changes for the different quiz cards.

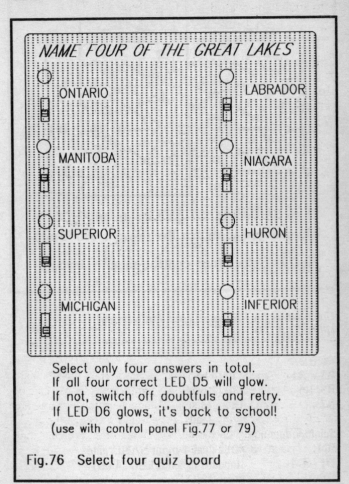

NAME FOUR OF THE GREAT LAKES

ONTARIO   LABRADOR

MANITOBA   NIAGARA

SUPERIOR   HURON

MICHIGAN   INFERIOR

Select only four answers in total.
If all four correct LED D5 will glow.
If not, switch off doubtfuls and retry.
If LED D6 glows, it's back to school!
(use with control panel Fig.77 or 79)

Fig.76 Select four quiz board

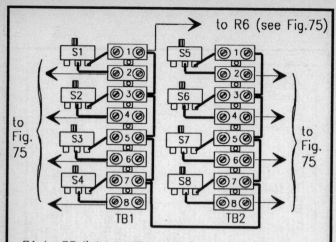

S1 to S8 links to IC1 gate inputs on Fig.75
interchanged to match the relevant quiz card

Fig.77 Select four control panel — layout

Components for Project 34 (standard version)
(Figs. 74 & 75)

Resistors

R1 – R4	470 (4 off)
R5, R6	270 (2 off)
R7	1k

Semiconductors

IC1	4012 dual 4-input NAND gate
D1 – D4	standard or axial LED (4 off)
D5	green LED
D6	red LED

Switches

S1 – S8	S.P.S.T. (select) (8 off)
S9	S.P.S.T. (on/off)

120

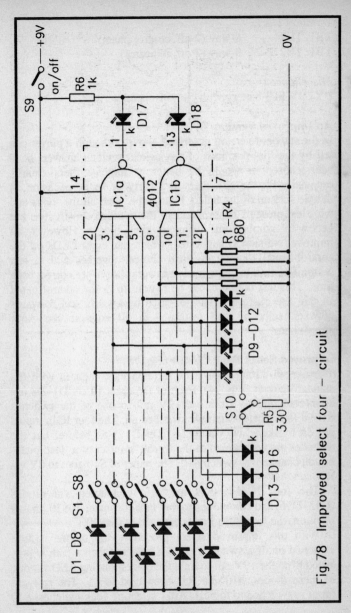

Fig.78 Improved select four – circuit

Terminal blocks

| TB1, TB2 | 8-way (2 off, control panel) |
| TB1, TB2 | 9-way (2 off, indicator) |

Miscellaneous
BY1 9V PP3 battery with clip, insulated wiring.

An Improved Version

In the standard version described above, although a player can tell by the 'on' positions of the switches which answers have been chosen, it would be better to indicate them clearly, especially for the onlookers at a party or social occasion. A deluxe version of the Select Four game, with all the 'bells and whistles' presents no problem to the average constructor, but gets a bit cumbersome using terminal blocks. However, an improved version is suggested, which has eight LEDs on the control panel to indicate each choice, together with a test button for checking how many answers chosen are correct each time. This test button could be remote from the control panel so that the contestant has to move backwards and forwards between selecting and testing – it all adds to the party atmosphere!

Improved Select Four Circuit (Fig. 78)

The overall circuit shows the differences compared with the standard circuit (Fig. 74). Each of the eight LEDs D1–D8 are connected directly from the +9V rail to one of the switches S1–S8 to indicate which are switched on. The four IC1a inputs are each taken low via LEDs (D9–D12) as before, but the cathodes are commoned to the 'break' contact of a 'test' push-button changeover switch S10. The wiper of S10 goes to 0V via R5.

The four IC1a inputs are also connected via diodes (D13–D16) and commoned to the 'make' contact of S10. In this position, the four IC1a inputs are held at logic 0.

With this improved select procedure the circuit is first switched on. If a switch S1 to 4 is selected then a path is provided from the +9V rail to light the corresponding LED via one of these diodes, S10 and R5, connected to 0V. The relevant input is switched to logic 1. After selecting four switches, S10

122

is pressed to test how many answers are valid. These are indicated on LEDs D9–D12 that are now switched in place of diodes D13–D16. This switching circuit serves three purposes: to maintain a path for D1–D4 indicator lights; to keep any unswitched inputs low (logic 0); and to provide a test switch facility. For economy, the four diodes and S10 could be omitted and the 'test' LEDs screened by a mechanical flap or shutter to prevent the number of correct answers, or otherwise, being seen during selection. If the small axial LEDs are used for D9–D12 then masking these would be easy.

Apart from component values, the IC1b input stage is almost identical to that of Figure 74.

Improved Select Four Control Panel (Fig. 79)

This version of the control panel includes eight LEDs, one in series with each switch to indicate which answers are selected. Hence the need for two 10-way terminal blocks. The eight arrows (In) indicate the connections to the IC1a and IC1b gates (see Figures 78 and 79a).

Components for Project 34 (improved version)
(Figs. 78 & 79)

Resistors
R1 – R4   680 ohms (4 off)
R5   330 ohms
R6   1k

Semiconductors
IC1   4012 dual 4-input NAND gate
D1 – D8   LED (8 off)
D9 – D12   standard or axial LED (4 off)
D13 – D16   1N4148 signal diode (4 off)
D17   green LED
D18   red LED

Switches
S1 – S8   S.P.S.T. (8 off)

| S9 | S.P.S.T. (on/off) |
| S10 | push-button changeover |

Terminal blocks

| TB1, TB2 | 10-way (2 off, control panel) (Fig. 79) |
| TB1, TB2 | 9/10-way (2 off, indicator) (Fig. 79a) |

Miscellaneous
BY1 9V PP3 battery with clip, insulating wire.

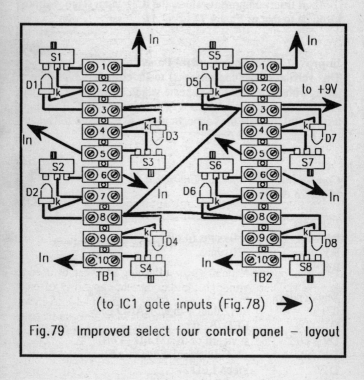

Fig.79 Improved select four control panel — layout

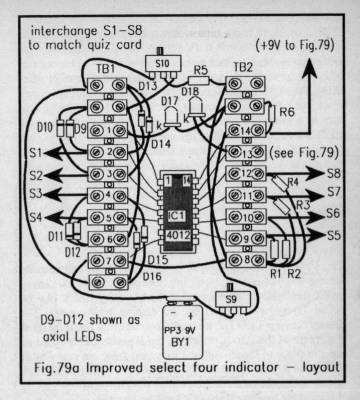

Fig.79a Improved select four indicator — layout

Project 35 – Twinkling Christmas Decorations

This final project reiterates how a flashing LED can be used to drive a counter. Although the d.c. current capability of each input or output of a 4000 series IC is limited to 10mA maximum, each of the ten outputs of the 4017 counter can be used with driver transistors to power a LED array, operate relays, or drive more powerful lamp displays. Here is the basic counter circuit driving five tri-colour LEDs and a standard LED from a LED that has a flashing rate of about twice per second. Adorn your Christmas table with one of these to make your guests wax lyrically, 'Twinkle, twinkle, little star, How I wonder what you are ...'. 'Well, actually, it's a souped-up decade counter firing on all cylinders ...'.

125

Circuit (Fig. 80)

Ordinarily, there is no need to use a limiting resistor with the flashing LED D6 across a 9V battery, but as we are using the LED to provide 2Hz clock pulses for input pin 14 of the counter IC1, R1 serves as a load. As explained in previous projects using the 4017 decade counter, the outputs go high for one clock cycle in sequence, causing the LEDs D1 to D5 to flash in turn in a green/red pattern at the same speed as the flashing LED D6. As the reset (pin 15) and clock enable (pin 13) are connected to 0V, the sequence restarts after the tenth output pulse. Pin 12 of IC1 is the carry out terminal, and is high during the first five output pulses and low for the second five. The LED, D7, on this output is therefore on alternately for five pulses and off for five pulses.

Layout (Fig. 81)

Two 9-way terminal blocks, TB2, TB3, provide the connections for the 4017 counter IC1 and the flashing LED D6. A 12-way and a single block are shown for the tri-colour LEDs, but the actual layout will depend on the display arrangement. The slower flashing LED D7, the really odd one out, could be set at the centre of the star. If preferred, ten separate LEDs could be used in place of the tri-colour LEDs, and there are many other variations on this theme. Ten series strings of three LEDs each could be connected from the outputs directly to the 0V rail; in this case the limiting resistor R3 can be omitted.

Components for Project 35
(Figs. 80 & 81)

Resistors

R1 – R3   1k (3 off)

Semiconductors

IC1   4017 decade counter
D1 – D5   tri-colour LED (5 off) (see text)
D6   flashing LED
D7   LED

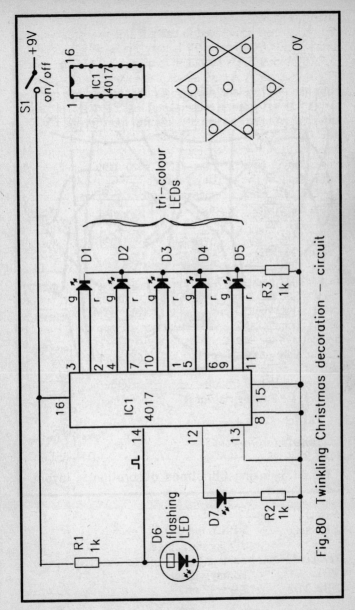

Fig.80 Twinkling Christmas decoration — circuit

127

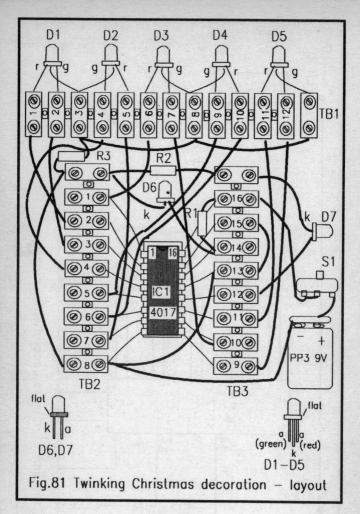

Fig.81 Twinking Christmas decoration — layout

Switch
S1   S.P.S.T. (on off)

Terminal blocks
TB1   12-way + single
TB2, TB3   9-way (2 off)

Miscellaneous
BY1 9V PP3 battery and clip, display material, insulated wiring.

Notes

133

Please Note

Babani Radio, Electronics and Computer books should be available from all good Booksellers, Radio Component Dealers and Mail Order Companies.

However, should you experience difficulty in obtaining any title in your area, then please write directly to the Publisher enclosing payment to cover the cost of the book plus adequate postage.

If you would like a complete catalogue of our entire range of Radio, Electronics and Computer Books then please send a Stamped Addressed Envelope to:

BERNARD BABANI (publishing) LTD
THE GRAMPIANS
SHEPHERDS BUSH ROAD
LONDON W6 7NF
ENGLAND